Succeed

Eureka Math®
Grade 3
Modules 3 & 4

TEKS EDITION

Great Minds® is the creator of *Eureka Math*®, *Wit & Wisdom*®, *Alexandria Plan*™, and *PhD Science*®.

Published by Great Minds PBC
greatminds.org

Printed in the USA

1 2 3 4 5 6 7 8 9 10 CCR 25 24 23 22

ISBN 978-1-63642-864-2

Learn ◆ Practice ◆ Succeed

Eureka Math® student materials for *A Story of Units®* (K–5) are available in the *Learn, Practice, Succeed* trio. This series supports differentiation and remediation while keeping student materials organized and accessible. Educators will find that the *Learn, Practice,* and *Succeed* series also offers coherent—and therefore, more effective—resources for Response to Intervention (RTI), extra practice, and summer learning.

Learn

Eureka Math Learn serves as a student's in-class companion where they show their thinking, share what they know, and watch their knowledge build every day. *Learn* assembles the daily classwork—Application Problems, Exit Tickets, Problem Sets, templates—in an easily stored and navigated volume.

Practice

Each *Eureka Math* lesson begins with a series of energetic, joyous fluency activities, including those found in *Eureka Math Practice.* Students who are fluent in their math facts can master more material more deeply. With *Practice,* students build competence in newly acquired skills and reinforce previous learning in preparation for the next lesson.

Together, *Learn* and *Practice* provide all the print materials students will use for their core math instruction.

Succeed

Eureka Math Succeed enables students to work individually toward mastery. These additional problem sets align lesson by lesson with classroom instruction, making them ideal for use as homework or extra practice. Each problem set is accompanied by a Homework Helper, a set of worked examples that illustrate how to solve similar problems.

Teachers and tutors can use *Succeed* books from prior grade levels as curriculum-consistent tools for filling gaps in foundational knowledge. Students will thrive and progress more quickly as familiar models facilitate connections to their current grade-level content.

Students, families, and educators:

Thank you for being part of the *Eureka Math*® community, where we celebrate the joy, wonder, and thrill of mathematics.

Nothing beats the satisfaction of success—the more competent students become, the greater their motivation and engagement. The *Eureka Math Succeed* book provides the guidance and extra practice students need to shore up foundational knowledge and build mastery with new material.

What is in the Succeed *book?*

Eureka Math Succeed books deliver supported practice sets that parallel the lessons of *A Story of Units*®. Each *Succeed* lesson begins with a set of worked examples, called *Homework Helpers*, that illustrate the modeling and reasoning the curriculum uses to build understanding. Next, students receive scaffolded practice through a series of problems carefully sequenced to begin from a place of confidence and add incremental complexity.

How should Succeed *be used?*

The collection of *Succeed* books can be used as differentiated instruction, practice, homework, or intervention. When coupled with *Affirm*®, *Eureka Math*'s digital assessment system, *Succeed* lessons enable educators to give targeted practice and to assess student progress. *Succeed*'s perfect alignment with the mathematical models and language used across *A Story of Units* ensures that students feel the connections and relevance to their daily instruction, whether they are working on foundational skills or getting extra practice on the current topic.

Where can I learn more about Eureka Math *resources?*

The Great Minds® team is committed to supporting students, families, and educators with an ever-growing library of resources, available at gm.greatminds.org/math-for-texas. The website also offers inspiring stories of success in the *Eureka Math* community. Share your insights and accomplishments with fellow users by becoming a *Eureka Math* Champion.

Best wishes for a year filled with Eureka moments!

Jill Diniz

Jill Diniz
Director of Mathematics
Great Minds

Contents

Module 3: Multiplication and Division with Units of 0, 1, 6–9, and Multiples of 10

Topic A: Multiplication as Comparison

Lesson 1 3

Lesson 2 7

Lesson 3 11

Lesson 4 15

Topic B: The Properties of Multiplication and Division

Lesson 5 19

Lesson 6 23

Lesson 7 27

Topic C: Multiplication and Division Using Units of 6 and 7

Lesson 8 31

Lesson 9 35

Lesson 10 39

Topic D: Multiplication and Division Using Units up to 8

Lesson 11 43

Lesson 12 47

Topic E: Multiplication and Division Using Units of 9

Lesson 13 51

Lesson 14 55

Topic F: Analysis of Patterns and Problem Solving Including Units of 0 and 1

Lesson 15 59

Lesson 16 63

Lesson 17 69

Topic G: Multiplication of Single-Digit Factors and Two-Digit Factors

Lesson 18 73

Lesson 19 77

Lesson 20 81

Lesson 21 89

Lesson 22 95

Lesson 23 99

Module 4: Multiplication and Area

Topic A: Concepts of Area Measurement

Lesson 1 105

Lesson 2 109

Lesson 3 113

Lesson 4 117

Lesson 5 121

Topic B: Arithmetic Properties Using Area Models

Lesson 6 125

Lesson 7 129

Lesson 8 133

Topic C: Applications of Area Using Side Lengths of Figures

Lesson 9 137

Lesson 10 141

Lesson 11 145

Lesson 12 149

Lesson 13 153

Grade 3
Module 3

Use strips of paper to solve. Sketch and label your work. Write an equation that matches the problem. The first one was done for you.

A blue paper strip is 3 times as long as a red paper strip. If the red paper strip is 1 unit long, how long is the blue paper strip?

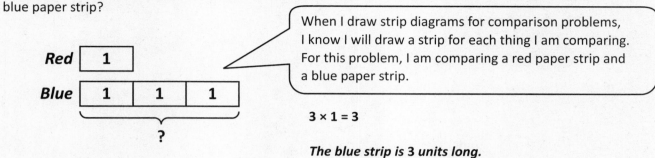

When I draw strip diagrams for comparison problems, I know I will draw a strip for each thing I am comparing. For this problem, I am comparing a red paper strip and a blue paper strip.

$3 \times 1 = 3$

The blue strip is 3 units long.

1. A blue paper strip is one unit long. A red paper strip is 4 times as long as the blue paper strip. How long is the red paper strip?

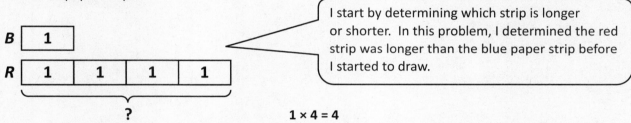

I start by determining which strip is longer or shorter. In this problem, I determined the red strip was longer than the blue paper strip before I started to draw.

$1 \times 4 = 4$

The red strip is 4 units long.

2. A red paper strip is 5 units long. The red paper strip is 5 times as long as the yellow paper strip. How long is the yellow paper strip?

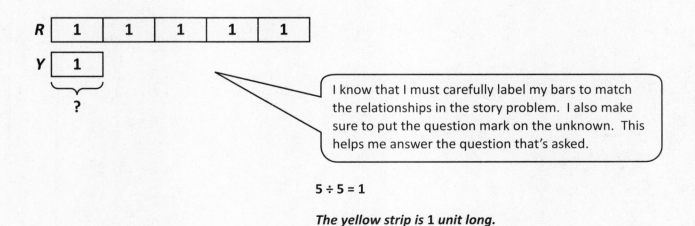

I know that I must carefully label my bars to match the relationships in the story problem. I also make sure to put the question mark on the unknown. This helps me answer the question that's asked.

$5 \div 5 = 1$

The yellow strip is 1 unit long.

Name _____　Date _____

Sketch and label your work. Write an equation that matches the problem. A sample has been done for you.

A red paper strip is 4 times as long as a blue paper strip. If the blue paper strip is 1 unit long, how long is the red paper strip?

Blue [1]　　　　　　　　　　　　　　　$4 \times 1 = 4$

Red [| | |]

?　　　　　The red strip is 4 units long.

1.　A red paper strip is 1 unit long. A blue paper strip is 5 times as long as the red paper strip. How long is the blue paper strip?

2.　The length of a red paper strip is double the length of a blue paper strip. The blue paper strip is 1 unit long. How long is the red paper strip?

3.　A red paper strip is 3 units long. The red paper strip is 3 times as long as the blue paper strip. How long is the blue paper strip?

Lesson 1:　　　Use multiplication to compare.

4. A yellow paper strip is 1 unit long. A red paper strip is 4 times as long as the yellow paper strip. A blue paper strip is 2 times as long as the red paper strip. How long is the blue paper strip? How many times longer is the red paper strip than the yellow paper strip?

5. Kevin bought a comic for 1 dollar. Elise bought a book for 5 times as much as Kevin's comic. How much did Elise pay for her book?

6. A yellow paper strip is 1 unit long. A blue paper strip is 4 times as long as the yellow paper strip. How long is the blue paper strip?

The sketch shows Seth's work. Explain his mistake.

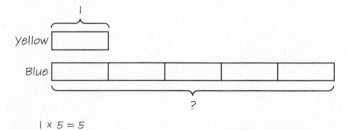

1 × 5 = 5

The blue paper strip is 5 units long.

EUREKA MATH
TEKS EDITION

Solve. Show your work with strip diagrams and an equation.

1. A blue paper strip is 9 centimeters long. A green paper strip is twice as long as the blue paper strip. How long is the green paper strip?

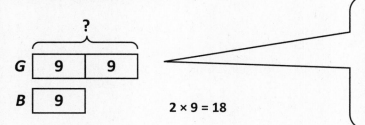

$2 \times 9 = 18$

> I can draw one unit of 9 to represent my blue paper strip and two units of 9 to represent my green paper strip. Then I use a multiplication equation to find the length of the green paper strip.

*The green paper strip is **18** centimeters long.*

2. An oak tree is 40 feet tall. It is 4 times taller than the top of the flag pole. How tall is the flag pole?

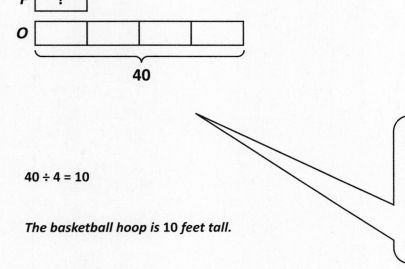

$40 \div 4 = 10$

*The basketball hoop is **10** feet tall.*

> This problem is different than the last because I'm given the total amount for the longer strip. I know from the story that there are 4 equal units inside the longer strip. These units are the same size as the unit that represents the flag pole.

Name _____   Date _____

Solve. Show your work with strip diagrams and an equation.

1. A red paper strip is 7 inches long. A yellow paper strip is twice as long as the red paper strip. How long is the yellow paper strip?

2. The ride to the zoo is 4 times as long as the ride to the art museum. If the ride to the art museum is 6 miles, how many miles is the ride to the zoo?

3. Wayne and Judy both collect sports cards. Wayne has 9 cards. Judy has 3 times as many cards as Wayne. How many sports cards does Judy have?

Lesson 2:   Use multiplication to compare.

EUREKA MATH
TEKS EDITION

4. The lake is 36 feet deep at its deepest point. That is 4 times as deep as the deep end at the community pool. How deep is the deepest part of the community pool?

5. Three friends went fishing. Hannah caught 3 times as many fish as Leslie. Shannon caught twice as many fish as Leslie. Leslie caught 2 fish. How many fish did the three friends catch in all?

6. Eleanora has 3 dogs. Her poodle weighs about 3 times more than her Yorkie. Her Russell terrier's weight is double the weight of her poodle. If the Russell terrier weighs 18 pounds, how much does the poodle weigh, and how much does the Yorkie weigh?

EUREKA MATH
TEKS EDITION

Fill in these in/out tables with the rule that's given.

1. The number that comes out of the box is 2 times
    as much as the number that went in to the box.

> Because the numbers that come out are 2 times the numbers that go in, I knew every number in the In column had to be multiplied by 2. Every number in the Out column had to be divided by 2.

In	Out
1	**2**
2	**4**
3	6
4	**8**
5	**10**
10	20

Complete the table. Then, complete the sentence using the words *times as much*.

2.

> The rows that are filled in help me see how the numbers that come out compare to the numbers that go in. To fill in the rest of this table, I had to either multiply by 4 or divide by 4.

In	Out
8	32
3	**12**
5	20
9	36
1	**4**

Rule:

The number that comes out is ___*four times as much*___ as the number that went in to the box.

Name _____   Date _____

The tables show what happens when a magician's box uses a rule to change numbers. Complete the tables using the rule that is given for each box.

1. The number that comes out of the box is 5 times as much as the number that went into the box.

In	Out
1	
2	
	15
4	
5	
	50

2. The number that comes out of the box is 3 times as much as the number that went into the box.

In	Out
1	
	6
	9
4	
5	
10	

3. The number that comes out of the box is 4 times as much as the number that went into the box.

In		9	5		1	
Out	24			40		32

Complete the table. Then, complete the sentence using the words *times as much.*

4.

In	Out
8	80
3	
	40
9	90
10	

Rule: The number that comes out of the box is _____
as the number that went in to the box.

5.

In	Out
7	35
2	
	45
6	30
1	

Rule: The number that comes out of the box is _____
as the number that went in to the box.

6. A magician put 8 cards into his magic box. 16 cards came out. Use the words *times as much* to compare 16 and 8.

Lesson 3:   Use tables to record multiplicative relationships.

Solve. Show your work by drawing strip diagrams.

1. Two friends like to look for shells on the beach. Kristie found 6 shells and Carlos found 4 times as much Kristie. How many shells did Carlos find?

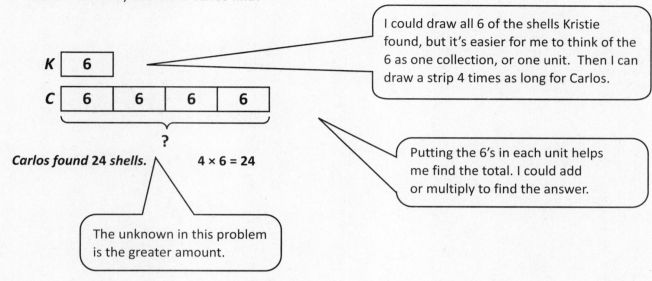

I could draw all 6 of the shells Kristie found, but it's easier for me to think of the 6 as one collection, or one unit. Then I can draw a strip 4 times as long for Carlos.

Putting the 6's in each unit helps me find the total. I could add or multiply to find the answer.

Carlos found 24 shells.   4 × 6 = 24

The unknown in this problem is the greater amount.

2. Jonathon went for a walk on Monday and Thursday. On Thursday, he walked 6 times as far as he did on Monday. If he walked 12 miles on Thursday, how far did he walk on Monday?

This problem tells me the greater number. I need to find the smaller amount.

One way to solve this problem is to use division. I could also think 6 times *something* equals 12.

12 ÷ 6 = 2

6 × ? = 12

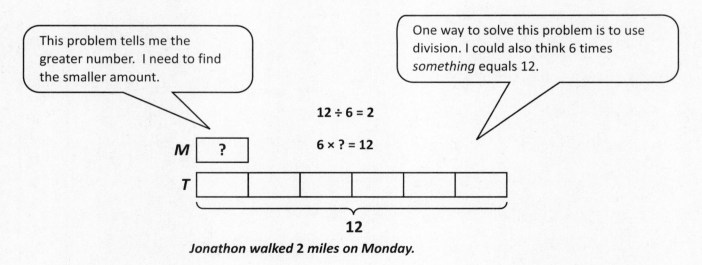

12

Jonathon walked 2 miles on Monday.

Solve. Show your work by drawing strip diagrams.

1. Jean earned $9 last week. This week, she earned 5 times as much as she did last week. How much money did Jean earn this week?

2. Fred went fishing on Saturday and Sunday. He caught 3 times as many fish on Saturday than he did on Sunday. If he caught 9 fish on Saturday, how many fish did Fred catch on Sunday?

3. Danny planted a garden with 8 plants. Harry planted a garden with 32 plants. How many times more plants did Harry plant than Danny?

4. Mr. Peterson will need 2 gallons of paint to paint his kitchen. He will need 2 times that amount to paint his bedroom and 5 times that amount to paint his livingroom. If he wants to paint all three rooms, how many gallons of paint does Mr. Peterson need?

5. The average life span of a parrot is 80 years. That is 8 times as much as the average life span of a green frog. The average life span of a horse is 4 times that of a green frog. What is the average life span of a green frog? What is the average life span of a horse?

Lesson 4:   Solve multiplicative comparison word problems.

EUREKA
MATH
TEKS EDITION

1. Write two multiplication facts for each array.

This array shows 3 rows of 7 dots, or 3 sevens. 3 sevens can be written as $3 \times 7 = 21$. I can also write it as $7 \times 3 = 21$ using the commutative property.

$\underline{\ \ 21\ \ } = \underline{\ \ 3\ \ } \times \underline{\ \ 7\ \ }$

$\underline{\ \ 21\ \ } = \underline{\ \ 7\ \ } \times \underline{\ \ 3\ \ }$

2. Match the expressions.

a. 4×7 6 threes

b. 3 sixes 7×4

The commutative property says that even if the order of the factors changes, the product stays the same!

3. Complete the equations.

a. $7 \times \underline{\ 2\ } = \underline{\ 7\ } \times 2$

$= \underline{\ 14\ }$

This equation shows that both sides equal the same amount. Since the factors 7 and 2 are already given, I just have to fill in the unknowns with the correct factors to show that each side equals 14.

b. 6 twos + 2 twos = $\underline{\ 8\ } \times \underline{\ 2\ }$

$= \underline{\ 16\ }$

This equation shows the break apart and distribute strategy that I learned in Module 1. 6 twos + 2 twos = 8 twos, or 8×2. Since I know $2 \times 8 = 16$, I also know $8 \times 2 = 16$ using commutativity. Using commutativity as a strategy allows me to know many more facts than the ones I've practiced before.

Name _____   Date _____

1. Complete the tables below.

   a. A tricycle has 3 wheels.

Number of Tricycles	3		5		7
Total Number of Wheels		12		18	

   b. A tiger has 4 legs.

Number of Tigers			7	8	9
Total Number of Legs	20	24			

   c. A package has 5 erasers.

Number of Packages	6				10
Total Number of Erasers		35	40	45	

2. Write two multiplication facts for each array.

   ⬠⬠⬠⬠⬠⬠
   ⬠⬠⬠⬠⬠⬠
   ⬠⬠⬠⬠⬠⬠
   ⬠⬠⬠⬠⬠⬠

   _____ = _____ × _____

   _____ = _____ × _____

   ●●●●●●●●
   ●●●●●●●●
   ●●●●●●●●

   _____ = _____ × _____

   _____ = _____ × _____

Lesson 5: Study commutativity to find known facts of 6, 7, 8, and 9.

21

3. Match the expressions.

    3×6 7 threes

    3 sevens 2×10

    2 eights 9×5

    5×9 8×2

    10 twos 6×3

4. Complete the equations.

    a. 2 sixes = _____ twos   b. _____ × 6 = 6 threes

        = ___12___   = _____

    c. $4 \times 8 =$ _____ $\times 4$ d. $4 \times$ _____ = _____ $\times 4$

        = _____   = ___28___

    e. 5 twos + 2 twos = _____ × _____   f. _____ fives + 1 five = 6×5

        = _____   = _____

Lesson 5:   Study commutativity to find known facts of 6, 7, 8, and 9.

1. Each has a value of 8.

> I know each block has a value of 8, so this tower shows 6 eights.

Unit form: 6 eights = __5__ eights + __1__ eight

$$= 40 + \underline{\ 8\ }$$

$$= \underline{\ 48\ }$$

> The shaded and unshaded blocks show 6 eights broken into 5 eights and 1 eight. These two smaller facts will help me solve the larger fact.

Facts:

$$\underline{\ 6\ } \times \underline{\ 8\ } = \underline{\ 48\ }$$

$$\underline{\ 8\ } \times \underline{\ 6\ } = \underline{\ 48\ }$$

> Using commutativity, I can solve 2 multiplication facts, 6×8 and 8×6, which both equal 48.

2. There are 7 blades on each pinwheel. How many total blades are on 8 pinwheels? Use a fives fact to solve.

> I need to find the value of 8×7, or 8 sevens. I can draw a picture. Each dot has a value of 7. I can use my familiar fives facts to break up 8 sevens as 5 sevens and 3 sevens.

$$8 \times 7 = (5 \times 7) + (3 \times 7)$$

$$= 35 + 21$$

$$= 56$$

> This is how I write the larger fact as the sum of two smaller facts. I can add their products to find the answer to the larger fact. $8 \times 7 = 56$

5 sevens

$5 \times 7 = 35$

3 sevens

$3 \times 7 = 21$

There are 56 blades on 8 pinwheels.

Lesson 6:   Apply the distributive and commutative properties to relate multiplication facts $5 \times n + n$ to $6 \times n$ and $n \times 6$ where n is the size of the unit.

Name _____   Date _____

1. Each has a value of 9.

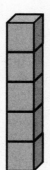

Unit form: _____

Facts: 5 × _____ = _____ × 5

Total = _____

_____

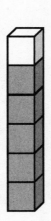

Unit form: 6 nines = _____ nines + _____ nine

= 45 + _____

= _____

Facts: _____ × _____ = _____

_____ × _____ = _____

Lesson 6:   Apply the distributive and commutative properties to relate multiplication facts 5 × n + n to 6 × n and n × 6 where n is the size of the unit.

© Great Minds PBC TEKS Edition |
greatminds.org/Texas

25

EUREKA MATH
TEKS EDITION

2. There are 6 blades on each windmill. How many total blades are on 7 windmills? Use a fives fact to solve.

---

3. Juanita organizes her magazines into 3 equal piles. She has a total of 18 magazines. How many magazines are in each pile?

---

4. Markuo spends $27 on some plants. Each plant costs $9. How many plants does he buy?

Lesson 6:   Apply the distributive and commutative properties to relate
multiplication facts $5 \times n + n$ to $6 \times n$ and $n \times 6$ where n is the size
of the unit.

© Great Minds PBC TEKS Edition |
greatminds.org/Texas

EUREKA
MATH
TEKS EDITION

1. Each equation contains a box representing the unknown. Find the value of the unknown.

$9 \div 3 = \square$	$\square = \underline{\ 3\ }$
$4 \times \square = 20$	$\square = \underline{\ 5\ }$

> I can think of this problem as division, $20 \div 4$, to find the unknown factor.

2. Brian buys 4 journals at the store for $8 each. What is the total amount Brian spends on 4 journals? Use a question mark to represent the total amount Brian spends, and then solve the problem.

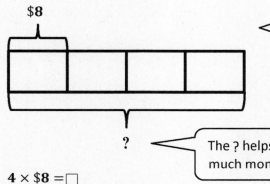

$8

?

> I can draw a strip diagram to help me solve this problem. From the diagram, I can see that I know the number of groups, 4, and the size of each group, $8, but I don't know the whole.

> The ? helps me label the unknown, which represents how much money Brian spends on 4 journals.

$4 \times \$8 = \square$

$\square = \$32$

Brian spends $32 on 4 journals.

Lesson 7: Multiply and divide with familiar facts using a box to represent the unknown.

27

Name _____   Date _____

1. a. Complete the pattern.

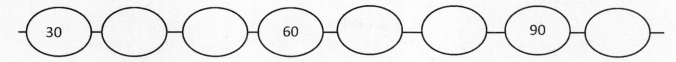

(30)─( )─( )─(60)─( )─( )─(90)─( )─

b. Find the value of the unknown.

$10 \times 2 = \square$ $\square = \underline{\;20\;}$ $10 \times 6 = \square$ $\square = \underline{\quad}$

$3 \times 10 = \square$ $\square = \underline{\quad}$ $10 \times 7 = \square$ $\square = \underline{\quad}$

$\square = 4 \times 10$ $\square = \underline{\quad}$ $\square = 8 \times 10$ $\square = \underline{\quad}$

$\square = 5 \times 10$ $\square = \underline{\quad}$

2. Find the value of the unknown.

$8 \div 2 = \square$	$\square = \underline{\quad}$
$3 \times \square = 12$	$\square = \underline{\quad}$
$\square \times 8 = 40$	$\square = \underline{\quad}$
$18 \div 6 = \square$	$\square = \underline{\quad}$
$\square \times 4 = 24$	$\square = \underline{\quad}$
$\square \div 7 = 5$	$\square = \underline{\quad}$
$6 \times 3 = \square$	$\square = \underline{\quad}$
$32 \div \square = 4$	$\square = \underline{\quad}$

Lesson 7:   Multiply and divide with familiar facts using a box to represent the unknown.

© Great Minds PBC TEKS Edition |
greatminds.org/Texas

3. Pedro buys 4 books at the fair for $7 each.

   a. What is the total amount Pedro spends on 4 books? Use a box to represent the total amount Pedro spends, and then solve the problem.

   b. Pedro hands the cashier 3 ten dollar bills. How much change will he receive? Write an equation to solve. Use a box to represent the unknown.

4. On field day, the first-grade dash is 25 meters long. The third-grade dash is twice the distance of the first-grade dash. How long is the third-grade dash? Use a box to represent the unknown and solve.

Lesson 7:   Multiply and divide with familiar facts using a box to represent the unknown.

EUREKA
MATH
TEKS EDITION

1. Use number bonds to help you skip-count by six by either making a ten or adding to the ones.

$60 + 6 =$ __66__

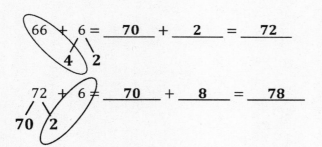

$66 + 6 =$ __70__ $+$ __2__ $=$ __72__

$72 + 6 =$ __70__ $+$ __8__ $=$ __78__

> I can break apart an addend to make a ten. For example, I see that 66 just needs 4 more to make 70. So I can break 6 into 4 and 2. Then $66 + 4 = 70$, plus 2 makes 72. It's much easier to add from a ten. Once I get really good at this, it'll make adding with mental math simple.

2. Count by six to fill in the blanks below.

6, __12__ , __18__ , __24__

> I can skip-count to see that 4 sixes make 24.

Complete the multiplication equation that represents your count-by.

$6 \times$ __4__ $=$ __24__

> 4 sixes make 24, so $6 \times 4 = 24$.

Complete the division equation that represents your count-by.

__24__ $\div 6 =$ __4__

> I'll use a related division fact. $6 \times 4 = 24$, so $24 \div 6 = 4$.

3. Count by six to solve $36 \div 6$. Show your work below.

$6, 12, 18, 24, 30, 36$

$36 \div 6 = 6$

> I'll skip-count by six until I get to 36. Then I can count to find the number of sixes it takes to make 36. It takes 6 sixes, so $36 \div 6 = 6$.

EUREKA MATH®
TEKS EDITION

Name _____   Date _____

1. Use number bonds to help you skip-count by six by either making a ten or adding to the ones.

a. 6 + 6 = __10__ + __2__ = _____
       /\
      4 2

b. 12 + 6 = __10__ + __8__ = _____
     /\
   10 2

c. 18 + 6 = _____ + _____ = _____
        /\
       2 4

d. 24 + 6 = _____ + _____ = _____
      /\
    20 4

e. 30 + 6 = _____

f. 36 + 6 = _____ + _____ = _____
        /\
       4 2

g. 42 + 6 = _____ + _____ = _____

h. 48 + 6 = _____ + _____ = _____

i. 54 + 6 = _____ + _____ = _____

2. Count by six to fill in the blanks below.

    6, _____, _____, _____, _____

    Complete the multiplication equation that represents the final number in your count-by.

    6 × _____ = _____

    Complete the division equation that represents your count-by.

    _____ ÷ 6 = _____

3. Count by six to fill in the blanks below.

    6, _____, _____, _____, _____, _____

    Complete the multiplication equation that represents the final number in your count-by.

    6 × _____ = _____

    Complete the division equation that represents your count-by.

    _____ ÷ 6 = _____

4. Count by six to solve 48 ÷ 6. Show your work below.

Lesson 8:   Count by units of 6 to multiply and divide using number bonds to decompose.

EUREKA MATH
TEKS EDITION

1. Use number bonds to help you skip-count by seven by either making a ten or adding to the ones.

   $70 + 7 =$ __**77**__

   $77 + 7 =$ __**80**__ $+$ __**4**__ $=$ __**84**__

   $3 \quad 4$

   $84 + 7 =$ __**90**__ $+$ __**1**__ $=$ __**91**__

   $6 \quad 1$

   > I can break apart an addend to make a ten. For example, I see that 77 just needs 3 more to make 80. So I can break 7 into 3 and 4. Then $77 + 3 = 80$, plus 4 makes 84. It's much easier to add from a ten. Once I get really good at this, it'll make adding with mental math simple.

2. Count by seven to fill in the blanks. Then use the multiplication equation to write the related division fact directly to its right.

   __**84**__ $7 \times 12 =$ __**84**__   __**84**__ $\div 7 =$ __**12**__

   __**77**__ $7 \times 11 =$ __**77**__   __**77**__ $\div 7 = 11$

   > I "climb" the ladder counting by sevens. The count-by helps me find the products of the multiplication facts. First I find the answer to the fact on the bottom rung. I record the answer in the equation and to the left of the ladder. Then I add seven to my answer to find the next number in my count-by. The next number in my count-by is the product of the next fact up on the ladder!

   > Once I find the product of a fact by skip-counting, I can write the related division fact. The total, or the product of the multiplication fact, gets divided by 7. The quotient represents the number of sevens I skip-counted.

EUREKA MATH
TEKS EDITION

Lesson 9:   Count by units of 7 to multiply and divide using number bonds to decompose.

35

Name _____ Date _____

1. Use number bonds to help you skip-count by seven by making ten or adding to the ones.

a. 7 + 7 = __10__ + __4__ = _____
       / \
      3   4

b. 14 + 7 = _____ + _____ = _____
        / \
       6   1

c. 21 + 7 = _____ + _____ = _____
     / \
   20   1

d. 28 + 7 = _____ + _____ = _____
        / \
       2   5

e. 35 + 7 = _____ + _____ = _____
        / \
       5   2

f. 42 + 7 = _____ + _____ = _____

g. 49 + 7 = _____ + _____ = _____

h. 56 + 7 = _____ + _____ = _____

Lesson 9:   Count by units of 7 to multiply and divide using number bonds to decompose.

37

2. Skip-count by seven to fill in the blanks. Then, fill in the multiplication equation, and use it to write the related division fact directly to the right.

_____	$7 \times 10 =$ _____	_____ $\div 7 =$ _____
_____	$7 \times 9 =$ _____	_____ $\div 7 =$ _____
_____	$7 \times 8 =$ _____	_____ $\div 7 =$ _____
49	$7 \times 7 =$ _____	_____ $\div 7 =$ _____
_____	$7 \times 6 =$ _____	_____ $\div 7 =$ _____
_____	$7 \times 5 =$ _____	_____ $\div 7 =$ _____
28	$7 \times 4 =$ _____	_____ $\div 7 =$ _____
_____	$7 \times 3 =$ _____	_____ $\div 7 =$ _____
_____	$7 \times 2 =$ _____	_____ $\div 7 =$ _____
7	$7 \times 1 =$ _____	_____ $\div 7 =$ _____

Lesson 9: Count by units of 7 to multiply and divide using number bonds to decompose.

EUREKA MATH
TEKS EDITION

1. Match the words on the arrow to the correct equation on the target.

7 times a number equals 56

$42 \div \square = 6$

> The equations use $\square$ to represent the unknown number. When I read the words on the left carefully, I can pick out the correct equation on the right.

42 divided by a number equals 6

$7 \times \square = 56$

2. Ari sells 7 boxes of pens at the school store.

    a. Each box of pens costs $6. Draw a strip diagram, and label the total amount of money Ari makes as $\square$ dollars. Write an equation, and solve for $\square$.

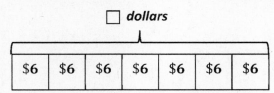

$\square$ *dollars*

| $6 | $6 | $6 | $6 | $6 | $6 | $6 |

$7 \times 6 = \square$

$\square = 42$

Ari makes* $42 *selling pens.

> I'm using a $\square$ to represent how much money Ari makes. Once I find the value of $\square$, then I know how much money Ari earns selling pens.

Lesson 10: Interpret the unknown in multiplication and division to model and solve problems using units of 6 and 7.

39

EUREKA MATH
TEKS EDITION

© Great Minds PBC TEKS Edition |
greatminds.org/Texas

b. Each box contains 8 pens. Draw a strip diagram, then write an equation, and solve for the unknown.

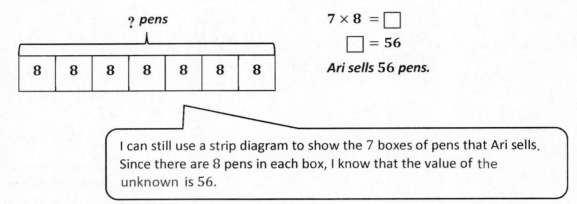

$7 \times 8 = \square$

$\square = 56$

Ari sells 56 pens.

> I can still use a strip diagram to show the 7 boxes of pens that Ari sells. Since there are 8 pens in each box, I know that the value of the unknown is 56.

3. Mr. Lucas divides 30 students into 6 equal groups for a project. Draw a strip diagram, then write an equation, and solve for the unknown.

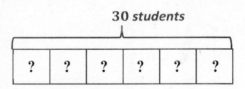

$30 \div 6 = \square$

$6 \times \square = 30$

$\square = 5$

There are 5 students in each group.

> I know that 30 students are split into 6 equal groups, so I have to solve $30 \div 6$ to figure out how many students are in each group. I'll use a question mark to represent the unknown. To solve, I can think about this as division or as an unknown factor problem.

Lesson 10:   Interpret the unknown in multiplication and division to model and solve problems using units of 6 and 7.

EUREKA MATH
TEKS EDITION

Name _____   Date _____

1. Match the words on the arrow to the correct equation on the target.

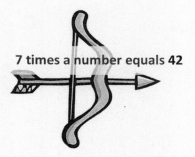
7 times a number equals 42

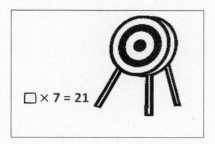
$\square \times 7 = 21$

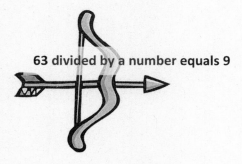
63 divided by a number equals 9

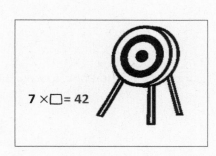
$7 \times \square = 42$

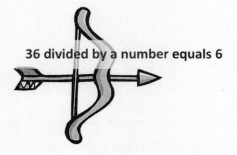
36 divided by a number equals 6

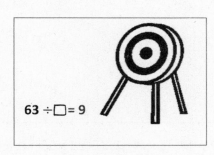
$63 \div \square = 9$

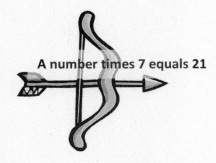
A number times 7 equals 21

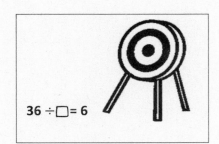
$36 \div \square = 6$

Lesson 10: Interpret the unknown in multiplication and division to model and solve problems using units of 6 and 7.

EUREKA MATH
TEKS EDITION

Model each problem with a drawing. Then, write an equation using a box to represent the unknown, and solve for the unknown.

2. Ari sells 6 boxes of pens at the school store.

   a. Each box of pens sells for $7. What is the total amount of money he makes?

   b. Each box contains 6 pens. How many pens are in all the boxes Ari sells?

3. Mr. Lucas divides 28 students into 7 equal groups for a project. How many students are in each group?

Lesson 10: Interpret the unknown in multiplication and division to model and solve problems using units of 6 and 7.

1. Solve.

   a. $9 - (6 + 3) = \underline{\ \ 0\ \ }$

   > I know the parentheses mean that I have to add $6 + 3$ first. Then I can subtract that sum from 9.

   b. $(9 - 6) + 3 = \underline{\ \ 6\ \ }$

   > I know the parentheses mean that I have to subtract $9 - 6$ first. Then I can add 3. The numbers in parts (a) and (b) are the same, but the answers are different because of where the parentheses are placed.

2. Use parentheses to make the equations true.

   a. $13 = 3 + (5 \times 2)$

   > I can put parentheses around 5×2. That means I first multiply 5×2, which equals 10, and then add 3 to get 13.

   b. $16 = (3 + 5) \times 2$

   > I can put parentheses around $3 + 5$. That means I first add $3 + 5$, which equals 8, and then multiply by 2 to get 16.

3. Determine if the equation is true or false.

a. $(4 + 5) \times 2 = 18$	*True*
b. $5 = 3 + (12 \div 3)$	*False*

   > I know part (a) is true because I can add $4 + 5$, which equals 9. Then I can multiply 9×2 to get 18.

   > I know part (b) is false because I can divide 12 by 3, which equals 4. Then I can add $4 + 3$. $4 + 3$ equals 7, not 5.

EUREKA MATH TEKS EDITION

© Great Minds PBC TEKS Edition | greatminds.org/Texas

4. Julie says that the answer to $16 + 10 - 3$ is 23 no matter where she puts the parentheses. Do you agree?

$(16 + 10) - 3 = 23$ $16 + (10 - 3) = 23$

I agree with Julie. I put parentheses around $16 + 10$, and when I solved the equation, I got 23 because $26 - 3 = 23$. Then I moved the parentheses and put them around $10 - 3$. When I subtracted $10 - 3$ first, I still got 23 because $16 + 7 = 23$. Even though I moved the parentheses, the answer didn't change!

Lesson 11:   Understand the function of parentheses and apply to solving problems.

Name _____ Date _____

1. Solve.

    a. 9 – (6 + 3) = _____

    b. (9 – 6) + 3 = _____

    c. _____ = 14 – (4 + 2)

    d. _____ = (14 – 4) + 2

    e. _____ = (4 + 3) × 6

    f. _____ = 4 + (3 × 6)

    g. (18 ÷ 3) + 6 = _____

    h. 18 ÷ (3 + 6) = _____

2. Use parentheses to make the equations true.

    a. 14 – 8 + 2 = 4

    b. 14 – 8 + 2 = 8

    c. 2 + 4 × 7 = 30

    d. 2 + 4 × 7 = 42

    e. 12 = 18 ÷ 3 × 2

    f. 3 = 18 ÷ 3 × 2

    g. 5 = 50 ÷ 5 × 2

    h. 20 = 50 ÷ 5 × 2

Lesson 11:   Understand the function of parentheses and apply to solving problems.

45

3. Determine if the equation is true or false.

a. $(15 - 3) \div 2 = 6$	*Example:* True
b. $(10 - 7) \times 6 = 18$	
c. $(35 - 7) \div 4 = 8$	
d. $28 = 4 \times (20 - 13)$	
e. $35 = (22 - 8) \div 5$	

4. Jerome finds that $(3 \times 6) \div 2$ and $18 \div 2$ are equal. Explain why this is true.

5. Place parentheses in the equation below so that you solve by finding the difference between 28 and 3. Write the answer.

$4 \times 7 - 3 =$ _____

6. Johnny says that the answer to $2 \times 6 \div 3$ is 4 no matter where he puts the parentheses. Do you agree? Place parentheses around different numbers to help you explain his thinking.

Lesson 11:   Understand the function of parentheses and apply to solving problems.

© Great Minds PBC TEKS Edition |
greatminds.org/Texas

EUREKA MATH
TEKS EDITION

1. Use the array to complete the equation.

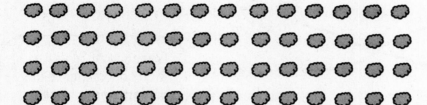

a. $4 \times 14 =$ __56__

> I can use the array to skip-count by 4 to find the product.

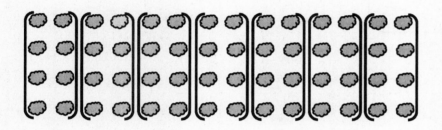

b. $(4 \times \underline{\ 2\ }) \times 7$

    $= \underline{\ \ 8\ \ } \times \underline{\ \ 7\ \ }$

    $= \underline{\ \ 56\ \ }$

> The array shows that there are 7 groups of 4×2.

> I rewrote 14 as 2×7. Then I moved the parentheses to make the equation $(4 \times 2) \times 7$. I can multiply 4×2 to get 8. Then I can multiply 8×7 to get 56. Rewriting 14 as 2×7 made the problem easier to solve!

2. Place parentheses in the equations to simplify and solve.

$3 \times 21 = 3 \times (3 \times 7)$

$= (3 \times 3) \times 7$ } $= \underline{\ \ 63\ \ }$

$= \underline{\ \ 9\ \ } \times 7$

> I can put the parentheses around 3×3 and then multiply. 3×3 equals 9. Now I can solve the easier multiplication fact, 9×7.

3. Solve. Then, match the related facts.

a. $24 \times 3 = \underline{\quad 72 \quad} = $ ————————— $9 \times (3 \times 2)$

b. $27 \times 2 = \underline{\quad 54 \quad} = $ ————————— $8 \times (3 \times 3)$

I can think of 24 as 8×3. Then, I can move the parentheses to make the new expression $8 \times (3 \times 3)$. $3 \times 3 = 9$, and $8 \times 9 = 72$, so $24 \times 3 = 72$.

I can think of 27 as 9×3. Then, I can move the parentheses to make the new expression $9 \times (3 \times 2)$. $3 \times 2 = 6$, and $9 \times 6 = 54$, so $27 \times 2 = 54$.

Lesson 12:   Model the associative property as a strategy to multiply.

EUREKA MATH
TEKS EDITION

Name _____   Date _____

1. Use the array to complete the equation.

a. $3 \times 16 =$ _____

b. $(3 \times$ _____$) \times 8$

= _____ $\times$ _____

= _____

c. $4 \times 18 =$ _____

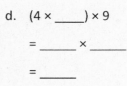

d. $(4 \times$ _____$) \times 9$

= _____ $\times$ _____

= _____

Lesson 12:   Model the associative property as a strategy to multiply.

49

EUREKA MATH
TEKS EDITION

2. Place parentheses in the equations to make it true. Then, solve.

$12 \times 4 = (6 \times 2) \times 4$

$\quad = 6 \times (2 \times 4)$ ⎤
⎥ = ___**48**___
$\quad = 6 \times \underline{\ 8\ }$ ⎦

a. $3 \times 14 = 3 \times (2 \times 7)$

$\quad = 3 \times 2 \times 7$ ⎤
⎥ = _____
$\quad = \underline{\quad} \times 7$ ⎦

b. $3 \times 12 = 3 \times (3 \times 4)$

$\quad = 3 \times 3 \times 4$ ⎤
⎥ = _____
$\quad = \underline{\quad} \times 4$ ⎦

3. Solve. Then, match the related facts.

a. $20 \times 2 = \underline{\ \ 40\ \ } =$ $6 \times (5 \times 2)$

b. $30 \times 2 = \underline{\quad} =$ $8 \times (5 \times 2)$

c. $35 \times 2 = \underline{\quad} =$ $4 \times (5 \times 2)$

d. $40 \times 2 = \underline{\quad} =$ $7 \times (5 \times 2)$

Lesson 12:   Model the associative property as a strategy to multiply.

EUREKA
MATH
TEKS EDITION

1. Each  has a value of 9. Find the value of each row. Then, add the rows to find the total.

$7 \times 9 =$ __63__

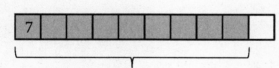

$5 \times 9 = 45$

__2__ $\times 9 =$ __18__

> I know each cube has a value of 9. The 2 rows of cubes show 7 nines broken up as 5 nines and 2 nines. It is the break apart and distribute strategy using the familiar fives fact.

$7 \times 9 = (5 + $ __2__ $) \times 9$

$= (5 \times 9) + ($ __2__ $\times 9)$

$= 45 +$ __18__

$=$ __63__

> To add 45 and 18, I'll simplify by taking 2 from 45. I'll add the 2 to 18 to make 20. Then I can think of the problem as $43 + 20$.

2. Find the total value of the shaded blocks.

$9 \times 7 =$

7								

9 sevens = 10 sevens – 1 seven

$=$ __70__ -7

$=$ __63__

> This shows a different way to solve. I can think of 7 nines as 9 sevens. 9 is closer to 10 than it is to 5. So instead of using a fives fact, I can use a tens fact to solve. I take the product of 10 sevens and subtract 1 seven.

> This strategy made the math simpler and more efficient. I can do $70 - 7$ quickly in my head!

EUREKA MATH
TEKS EDITION

Lesson 13:   Apply the distributive property and the fact $9 = 10 - 1$ as a strategy to multiply.

51

© Great Minds PBC TEKS Edition |
greatminds.org/Texas

3. James buys a pack of baseball cards. He counts 9 rows of 6 cards. He thinks of 10 sixes to find the total number of cards. Show the strategy that James might have used to find the total number of baseball cards.

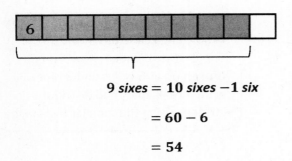

9 *sixes* = 10 *sixes* −1 *six*

$$= 60 - 6$$

$$= 54$$

James bought 54 *baseball cards.*

> James uses the tens fact to solve for the nines fact. To solve for 9 sixes, he starts with 10 sixes and subtracts 1 six.

Lesson 13: Apply the distributive property and the fact $9 = 10 - 1$ as a strategy to multiply.

EUREKA MATH
TEKS EDITION

Name _____ Date _____

1. Find the value of each row. Then, add the rows to find the total.

a. Each has a value of 6.

9 × 6 = _____

 5 × 6 = 30

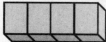 4 × 6 = _____

9 × 6 = (5 + 4) × 6
= (5 × 6) + (4 × 6)
= 30 + _____
= _____

b. Each has a value of 7.

9 × 7 = _____

 5 × 7 = _____

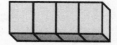 _____ × 7 = _____

9 × 7 = (5 + _____) × 7
= (5 × 7) + (_____ × 7)
= 35 + _____
= _____

c. Each has a value of 8.

9 × 8 = _____

 5 × 8 = _____

 _____ × 8 = _____

9 × 8 = (5 + _____) × 8
= (5 × 8) + (_____ × _____)
= 40 + _____
= _____

d. Each has a value of 9.

9 × 9 = _____

 5 × 9 = _____

 _____ × 9 = _____

9 × 9 = (5 + _____) × 9
= (5 × 9) + (_____ × _____)
= 45 + _____
= _____

Lesson 13: Apply the distributive property and the fact $9 = 10 - 1$ as a strategy to multiply.

2. Match.

a. **9 fives** = 10 fives − 1 five

   = 50 − 5

b. **9 sixes** = 10 sixes − 1 six

   =_____ − 6

c. **9 sevens** = 10 sevens − 1 seven

   = _____ − 7

d. **9 eights** = 10 eights − 1 eight

   = _____ − 8

e. **9 nines** = 10 nines − 1 nine

   = _____ − _____

f. **9 fours** = 10 fours − 1 four

   = _____ − _____

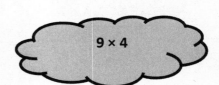

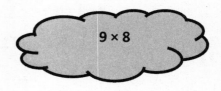

Lesson 13:   Apply the distributive property and the fact $9 = 10 − 1$ as a strategy to multiply.

EUREKA
MATH®
TEKS EDITION

Judy wants to give each of her friends a bag of 9 marbles. She has a total of 54 marbles. She runs to give them to her friends and gets so excited that she drops and loses 2 bags. How many total marbles does she have left to give away?

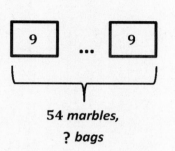

54 *marbles,*

? *bags*

> I can model the problem using a strip diagram. I know Judy has a total of 54 marbles, and each bag has 9 marbles. I don't know how many bags of marbles Judy has at first. Since I know the size of each group is 9 but I don't know the number of groups, I put a "…" in between the 2 units to show that I don't yet know how many groups, or units, to draw.

? represents the number of bags of marbles

$54 \div 9 = ?$

$? = 6$

> I can use a ? to represent the unknown, which is the number of bags Judy has at first. I can find the unknown by dividing 54 by 9 to get 6 bags. But 6 bags does not answer the question, so my work on this problem is not finished.

> Now I can redraw my model to show the 6 bags of marbles. I know that Judy drops and loses 2 bags. The unknown is the total number of marbles she has left to give away. I can represent this unknown with a ?.

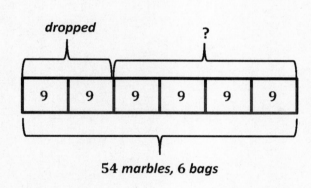

54 *marbles,* 6 *bags*

> From my diagram, I can see that Judy has 4 bags of 9 marbles left. I can choose any of my nines strategies to help me solve 4×9. $4 \times 9 = 36$, which means there are 36 total marbles left.

? represents the total number of marbles left

$4 \times 9 = ?$

$? = 36$

Judy still has 36 marbles left to give away.

> I read the problem carefully and made sure to answer with the total number of marbles, not the number of bags. Putting my answer in a statement helps me check that I've answered the problem correctly.

EUREKA MATH
TEKS EDITION

Lesson 14: Interpret the unknown in multiplication and division to model and solve problems.

55

© Great Minds PBC TEKS Edition |
greatminds.org/Texas

Name _____ Date _____

1. The store clerk equally divides 36 apples among 9 baskets. Draw a strip diagram, and label the number of apples in each basket with a question mark. Write an equation, and solve for the unknown.

2. Elijah gives each of his friends a pack of 9 almonds. He gives away a total of 45 almonds. How many packs of almonds did he give away? Model using a question mark or a box to represent the unknown, and then solve.

3. Denice buys 7 movies. Each movie costs $9. What is the total cost of 7 movies? Use an empty box to represent the unknown. Solve.

EUREKA MATH
TEKS EDITION

Lesson 14: Interpret the unknown in multiplication and division to model and solve problems.

© Great Minds PBC TEKS Edition | greatminds.org/Texas

57

4. Mr. Doyle shares 1 roll of bulletin board paper equally with 8 teachers. The total length of the roll is 72 meters. How much bulletin board paper does each teacher get?

5. There are 9 pens in a pack. Ms. Ochoa buys 9 packs. After giving her students some pens, she has 27 pens left. How many pens did she give away?

6. Allen buys 9 packs of trading cards. There are 10 cards in each pack. He can trade 30 cards for a comic book. How many comic books can he get if he trades all of his cards?

Lesson 14: Interpret the unknown in multiplication and division to model and solve problems.

© Great Minds PBC TEKS Edition | greatminds.org/Texas

1. Let ? = 4. Determine whether the equations are true or false.

a. ? × 0 = 0	**True**
b. 0 ÷ ? = 4	**False**
c. 1 × ? = 1	**False**
d. ? ÷ 1 = 4	**True**

I know this equation is false because 0 divided by any number is 0. If I put in any value for ? other than 0, the answer will be 0.

I know this is false because any number times 1 equals that number, not 1. This equation would be correct if it was written as 1 × ? = 4.

2. Elijah says that any number multiplied by 1 equals that number.

a. Write a multiplication equation using *c* to represent Elijah's statement.

   1 × ? = ?

   I can also use the commutative property to write my equation as ? × 1 = ?.

b. Using your equation from part (a), let ? = 6, and draw a picture to show that the new equation is true.

   My picture shows 1 group multiplied by ?, or 6. 1 group of 6 makes a total of 6. This works for any value, not just 6.

Lesson 15: Reason about and explain arithmetic patterns using units of 0 and 1 as they relate to multiplication and division.

59

EUREKA MATH
TEKS EDITION

© Great Minds PBC TEKS Edition |
greatminds.org/Texas

Name _____   Date _____

1. Complete.

a. $4 \times 1 =$ _____   b. $4 \times 0 =$ _____   c. _____ $\times 1 = 5$ d. _____ $\div 5 = 0$

e. $6 \times$ _____ $= 6$ f. _____ $\div 6 = 0$ g. $0 \div 7 =$ _____   h. $7 \times$ _____ $= 0$

i. $8 \div$ _____ $= 8$ j. _____ $\times 8 = 8$ k. $9 \times$ _____ $= 9$ l. $9 \div$ _____ $= 1$

2. Match each equation with its solution.

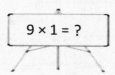

$9 \times 1 = ?$

$? \times 1 = 6$

$7 \div ? = 1$

$1 \times ? = 8$

$? \div 8 = 0$

$9 \div 9 = ?$

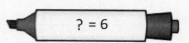

$? = 6$

$? = 7$

$? = 8$

$? = 9$

$? = 1$

$? = 0$

EUREKA
MATH
TEKS EDITION

Lesson 15:   Reason about and explain arithmetic patterns using units of 0 and 1 as
they relate to multiplication and division.

61

3. Let ? = 8. Determine whether the equations are true or false. The first one has been done for you.

a.	$? \times 0 = 8$	*False*
b.	$0 \times ? = 0$	
c.	$? \times 1 = 8$	
d.	$1 \times ? = 8$	
e.	$0 \div ? = 8$	
f.	$8 \div ? = 1$	
g.	$0 \div ? = 0$	
h.	$? \div 0 = 8$	

4. Rajan says that any number multiplied by 1 equals that number.

   a. Write a multiplication equation using *n* to represent Rajan's statement.

   b. Using your equation from Part (a), let *n* = 5, and draw a picture to show that the new equation is true.

Lesson 15:   Reason about and explain arithmetic patterns using units of 0 and 1 as they relate to multiplication and division.

EUREKA
MATH
TEKS EDITION

1. Explain how $8 \times 7 = (5 \times 7) + (3 \times 7)$ is shown in the multiplication table.

   The multiplication table shows $5 \times 7 = 35$ and $3 \times 7 = 21$. So, $35 + 21 = 56$, which is the product of 8×7.

   This is the break apart and distribute strategy. Using that strategy, I can add the products of 2 smaller facts to find the product of a larger fact.

2. Use what you know to find the product of 3×16.

   $3 \times 16 = (3 \times 8) + (3 \times 8)$
   $= 24 + 24$
   $= 48$

   I can also break up 3×16 as 10 threes + 6 threes, which is $30 + 18$. Or I can add 16 three times: $16 + 16 + 16$. I always want to use the most efficient strategy. This time it helped me to see the problem as double 24.

3. Today in class we found that $? \times ?$ is the sum of the first ? odd numbers. Use this pattern to find the value of ? for each equation below.

   a. $1 + 3 + 5 = ? \times ?$
      $9 = 3 \times 3$

   b. $1 + 3 + 5 + 7 = ? \times ?$
      $16 = 4 \times 4$

   The sum of the first 3 odd numbers is the same as the product of 3×3. The sum of the first 4 odd numbers is the same as the product of 4×4. The sum of the first 5 odd numbers is the same as the product of 5×5.

   c. $1 + 3 + 5 + 7 + 9 = ? \times ?$
      $25 = 5 \times 5$

   Wow, it's a pattern! I know that the first 6 odd numbers will be the same as the product of 6×6 and so on.

Name _____   Date _____

1. a. Write the products into the chart as fast as you can.

×	1	2	3	4	5	6	7	8
1								
2								
3								
4								
5								
6								
7								
8								

b. Color the rows and columns with even factors yellow.

c. What do you notice about the factors and products that are left unshaded?

EUREKA
MATH
TEKS EDITION

Lesson 16: Identify patterns in multiplication and division facts using the multiplication table.

© Great Minds PBC TEKS Edition |
greatminds.org/Texas

65

d. Complete the chart by filling in each blank and writing an example for each rule.

Rule	Example
odd times odd equals _____	
even times even equals _____	
even times odd equals _____	

e. Explain how $7 \times 6 = (5 \times 6) + (2 \times 6)$ is shown in the table.

f. Use what you know to find the product of 4×16 or 8 fours + 8 fours.

2. Today in class, we found that $n \times n$ is the sum of the first n odd numbers. Use this pattern to find the value of n for each equation below. The first is done for you.

a. $1 + 3 + 5 = n \times n$

$9 = 3 \times 3$

b. $1 + 3 + 5 + 7 = n \times n$

Lesson 16: Identify patterns in multiplication and division facts using the multiplication table.

EUREKA MATH
TEKS EDITION

c. $1 + 3 + 5 + 7 + 9 + 11 = n \times n$

d. $1 + 3 + 5 + 7 + 9 + 11 + 13 + 15 = n \times n$

e. $1 + 3 + 5 + 7 + 9 + 11 + 13 + 15 + 17 + 19 = n \times n$

Lesson 16: Identify patterns in multiplication and division facts using the multiplication table.

67

William has $187 in the bank. He saves the same amount of money each week for 6 weeks and puts it in the bank. Now William has $241 in the bank. How much money does William save each week?

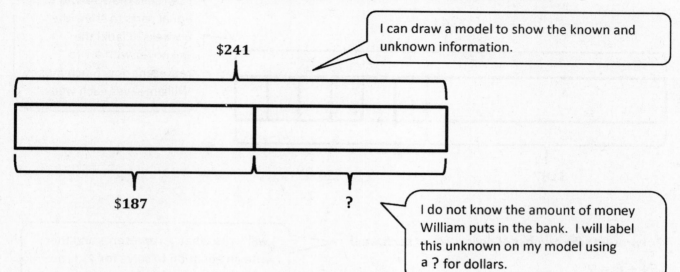

I can draw a model to show the known and unknown information.

$241

$187   **?**

I do not know the amount of money William puts in the bank. I will label this unknown on my model using a ? for dollars.

? represents the number of dollars William puts in the bank

$241 − $187 = ?

? = $54

I can write what ? represents and then write an equation to solve for ?. I can subtract the known part, $187, from the whole amount, $241, to find ?.

This answer is reasonable because $187 + $54 = $241. But it does not answer the question the problem asks. I'm trying to figure out how much money William saves each week, so I need to adjust my model.

Lesson 17:   Solve two-step word problems involving all four operations and assess the reasonableness of solutions.

69

EUREKA MATH
TEKS EDITION

© Great Minds PBC TEKS Edition |
greatminds.org/Texas

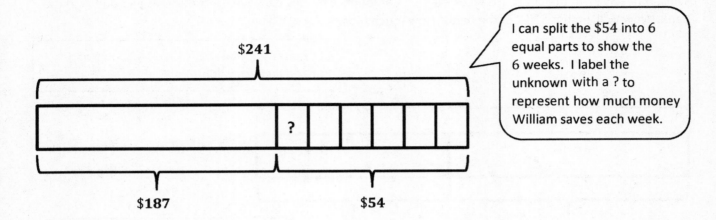

I can split the $54 into 6 equal parts to show the 6 weeks. I label the unknown with a ? to represent how much money William saves each week.

? represents the number of dollars saved each week

I will write what ? represents and then write an equation to solve for ?. I can divide $54 by 6 to get $9.

$54 \div 6 = ?$

$? = \$9$

William saves $9 each week.

My answer is reasonable because $9 a week for 6 weeks is $54. That's about $50. $187 is about $190. $190 + $50 = $240, which is very close to $241. My estimate is only $1 less than my answer!

I can explain why my answer is reasonable by estimating.

Lesson 17: Solve two-step word problems involving all four operations and assess the reasonableness of solutions.

EUREKA MATH
TEKS EDITION

Name _____   Date _____

Use the RDW process for each problem. Explain why your answer is reasonable.

1. Mrs. Portillo's cat weighs 6 kilograms. Her dog weighs 22 kilograms more than her cat. What is the total weight of her cat and dog?

2. Darren spends 39 minutes studying for his science test. He then does 6 chores. Each chore takes him 3 minutes. How many minutes does Darren spend studying and doing chores?

3. Mr. Abbot buys 8 boxes of granola bars for a party. Each box has 9 granola bars. After the party, there are 39 bars left. How many bars were eaten during the party?

EUREKA
MATH
TEKS EDITION

Lesson 17:   Solve two-step word problems involving all four operations and assess
             the reasonableness of solutions.

© Great Minds PBC TEKS Edition |
greatminds.org/Texas

71

4. Leslie weighs her marbles in a jar, and the scale reads 474 grams. The empty jar weighs 439 grams.
    Each marble weighs 5 grams. How many marbles are in the jar?

5. Kenny uses 72 centimeters of ribbon to wrap gifts. He uses 24 centimeters of his total ribbon to wrap
    a big gift. He uses the remaining ribbon for 6 small gifts. How much ribbon will he use for each small gift
    if he uses the same amount on each?

6. Six friends equally share the cost of a gift. They pay $90 and receive $42 in change. How much does each
    friend pay?

Lesson 17:   Solve two-step word problems involving all four operations and assess
the reasonableness of solutions.

1. Use the disks to fill in the blanks in the equations.

This array of disks shows 2 rows of 3 ones.

This array of disks shows 2 rows of 3 tens.

a.

2×3 ones = ___6___ ones

$2 \times 3 =$ ___6___

b.

2×3 tens = ___6___ tens

$2 \times 30 =$ ___60___

The top equations are written in unit form. The bottom equations are written in standard form. The 2 equations say the same thing.

I see that both arrays have the same number of disks. The only difference is the unit. The array on the left uses ones, and the array on the right uses tens.

Lesson 18: Multiply by multiples of ten using the place value chart.

73

EUREKA MATH
TEKS EDITION

> I see that the difference between Problems 1 and 2 is the model. Problem 1 uses place value disks. Problem 2 uses the chip model. With both models, I'm still multiplying ones and tens.

2. Use the chart to complete the blanks in the equations.

tens	ones
	• • • •
	• • • •
	• • • •

tens	ones
• • • •	
• • • •	
• • • •	

a. 3×4 ones = ___12___ ones

     3×4 = ___12___

b. 3×4 tens = ___12___ tens

     3×40 = ___120___

> I notice the number of dots is exactly the same in both charts. The difference between the charts is that when the units change from ones to tens, the dots shift over to the tens place.

3. Match.

80×2 ———————————— 160

> In order to solve a more complicated problem like this one, I can first think of it as 8 ones × 2, which is 16. Then all I need to do is move the answer over to the tens place so it becomes 16 tens. 16 tens is the same as 160.

Lesson 18:   Multiply by multiples of ten using the place value chart.

Name _____   Date _____

1. Use the disks to complete the blanks in the equations.

a.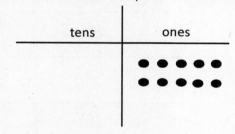

b.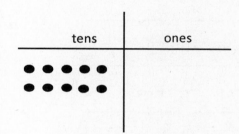

3×3 ones = _____ ones

3×3 = _____

3×3 tens = _____ tens

30×3 = _____

2. Use the chart to complete the blanks in the equations.

tens	ones
	• • • • •
	• • • • •

tens	ones
• • • • •	
• • • • •	

a. 2×5 ones = _____ ones

2×5 = _____

b. 2×5 tens = _____ tens

2×50 = _____

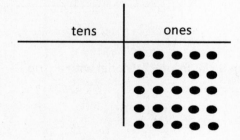

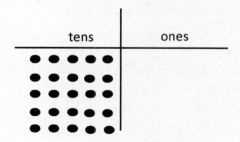

c. 5×5 ones = _____ ones

5×5 = _____

d. 5×5 tens = _____ tens

5×50 = _____

Lesson 18:   Multiply by multiples of ten using the place value chart.

75

© Great Minds PBC TEKS Edition |
greatminds.org/Texas

3. Match.

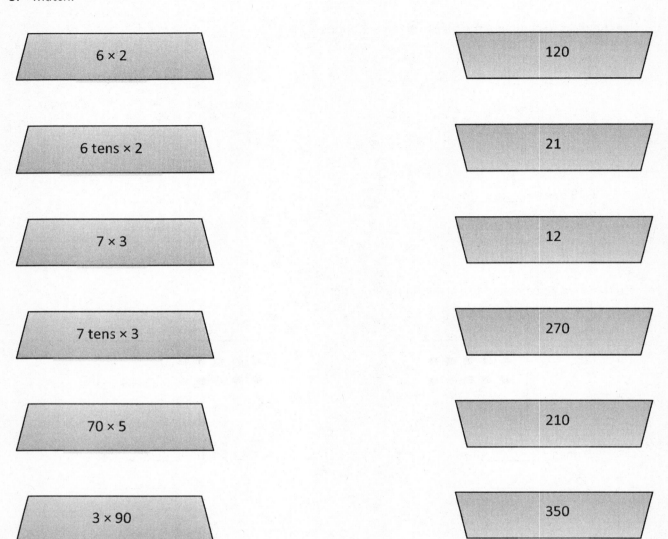

6 × 2		120
6 tens × 2		21
7 × 3		12
7 tens × 3		270
70 × 5		210
3 × 90		350

4. Each classroom has 30 desks. What is the total number of desks in 8 classrooms? Model with a strip diagram.

Lesson 18:   Multiply by multiples of ten using the place value chart.

EUREKA MATH
TEKS EDITION

1. Use the chart to complete the equations. Then solve.

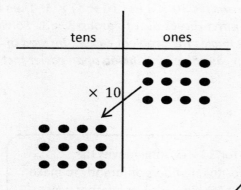

> I know that parentheses change the way numbers are grouped for solving. I can see that the parentheses group 3 × 4 ones, so I'll do that part of the equation first. 3 × 4 ones = 12 ones. Next I'll multiply the 12 ones by 10. The equation becomes 12 × 10 = 120. The chip model shows how I can multiply the 3 groups of 4 ones by 10.

a. $(3 \times 4) \times 10$

$= (12 \text{ ones}) \times 10$

$= \underline{\ \ 120\ \ }$

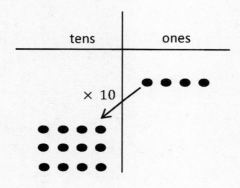

> I can see that here the parentheses move over and group the 4 ones × 10. I'll solve that first to get 40, or 4 tens. Then I can multiply the 4 tens by 3. So the equation becomes 3 × 40 = 120. The chip model shows how I multiply 4 ones by 10 first and then multiply the 4 tens by three.

b. $3 \times (4 \times 10)$

$= 3 \times (4 \text{ tens})$

$= \underline{\ \ 120\ \ }$

> By moving the parentheses over and grouping the numbers differently, this problem becomes friendlier. 3 × 40 is a little easier than multiplying 12 × 10. This new strategy will me help find larger unknown facts later on.

EUREKA
MATH
TEKS EDITION

2. John solves 30×3 by thinking about 10×9. Explain his strategy.

$$
\begin{aligned}
30 \times 3 &= (10 \times 3) \times 3 \\
&= 10 \times (3 \times 3) \\
&= 10 \times 9 \\
&= 90
\end{aligned}
$$

John writes 30×3 as $(10 \times 3) \times 3$. Then he moves the parentheses over to group 3×3. Solving $3 \cdot 3$ first makes the problem easier. Instead of 30×3, John can solve by thinking of an easier fact, 10×9.

Although it is easy to solve for 30×3, John moves the parentheses over and groups the numbers differently to make the problem a little friendlier for him. It's just another way to think about the problem.

Lesson 19:   Use place value strategies and the associative property $n \times (m \times 10) = (n \times m) \times 10$ (where n and m are less than 10) to multiply multiples of 10.

EUREKA MATH
TEKS EDITION

Name _____   Date _____

1. Use the chart to complete the equations. Then, solve.

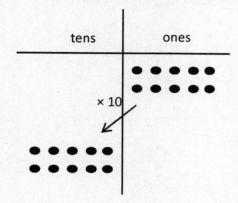

a. $(2 \times 5) \times 10$

= $(10 \text{ ones}) \times 10$

= _____

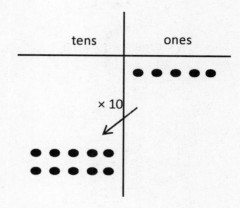

b. $2 \times (5 \times 10)$

= $2 \times (5 \text{ tens})$

= _____

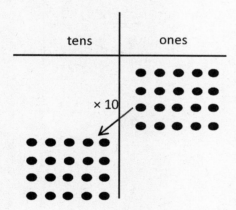

c. $(4 \times 5) \times 10$

= (_____ ones) $\times 10$

= _____

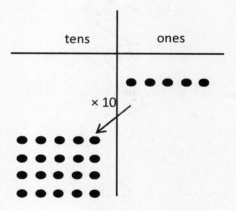

d. $4 \times (5 \times 10)$

= $4 \times ($_____ tens$)$

= _____

Lesson 19:   Use place value strategies and the associative property $n \times (m \times 10) =$
$(n \times m) \times 10$ (where n and m are less than 10) to multiply multiples of 10.

79

EUREKA
MATH®
TEKS EDITION

2. Solve. Place parentheses in (c) and (d) as needed to find the related fact.

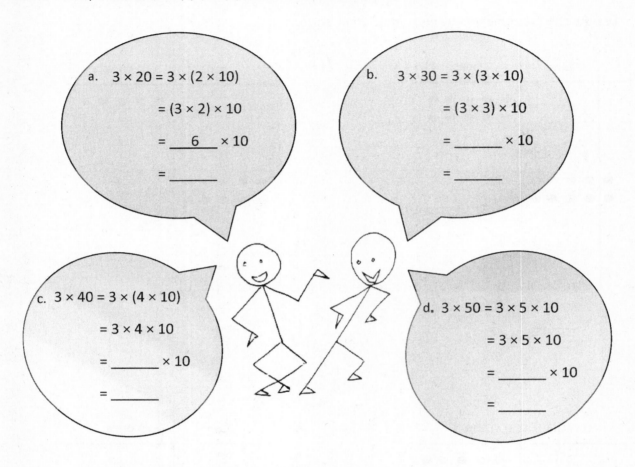

a. $3 \times 20 = 3 \times (2 \times 10)$

$= (3 \times 2) \times 10$

$= \underline{\quad 6 \quad} \times 10$

$= \underline{\qquad}$

b. $3 \times 30 = 3 \times (3 \times 10)$

$= (3 \times 3) \times 10$

$= \underline{\qquad} \times 10$

$= \underline{\qquad}$

c. $3 \times 40 = 3 \times (4 \times 10)$

$= 3 \times 4 \times 10$

$= \underline{\qquad} \times 10$

$= \underline{\qquad}$

d. $3 \times 50 = 3 \times 5 \times 10$

$= 3 \times 5 \times 10$

$= \underline{\qquad} \times 10$

$= \underline{\qquad}$

3. Danny solves 5×20 by thinking about 10×10. Explain his strategy.

Lesson 19:   Use place value strategies and the associative property $n \times (m \times 10) =$
$(n \times m) \times 10$ (where n and m are less than 10) to multiply multiples of 10.

EUREKA
MATH®
TEKS EDITION

1. Use your place value disks and charts to represent the following expressions. Record your work on the place value chart shown. Then write a matching expression, and record the partial products vertically.

    2 × 33

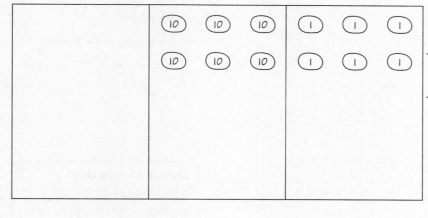

33
× 2
─────
    6 ← 2 × 3 ones
+ 60 ← 2 × 3 tens
─────
   66 ← 2 × 3 tens + 2 × 3 ones

> I use my place value chart to draw labeled disks that show 2 groups of 3 ones and 2 groups of 3 tens. This will help me record my partial products vertically and find total product.

    2 × 35

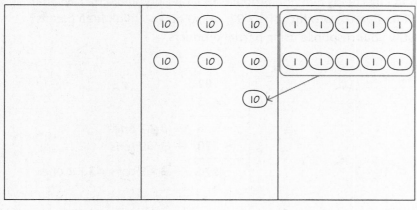

35
× 2
─────
   10 ← 2 × 5 ones
+ 60 ← 2 × 3 tens
─────
   70 ← 2 × 3 tens + 2 × 5 ones

> When I draw my labeled disks onto my place value chart, I can see that I have 10 ones. I know that I can regroup 10 ones into 1 ten, so I will circle the ten ones to show that I am making a new ten.

Lesson 20:   Use concrete models to represent two-digit by one-digit multiplication.

81

4 × 67

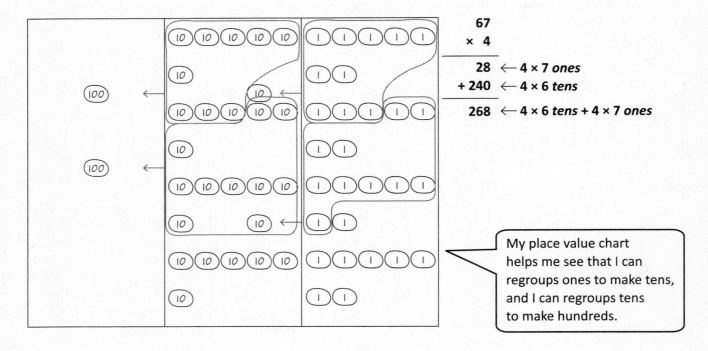

67
× 4

28 ← **4 × 7 ones**
+ 240 ← **4 × 6 tens**

268 ← **4 × 6 tens + 4 × 7 ones**

My place value chart helps me see that I can regroups ones to make tens, and I can regroups tens to make hundreds.

2. Juan says that knowing his multiplication facts helps him find products of larger numbers. He says that knowing 3 × 9 = 27 and 3 × 2 = 6 helps him find the product of 3 × 92. What do you think Juan means? Explain your thinking in words, and justify your response using partial products.

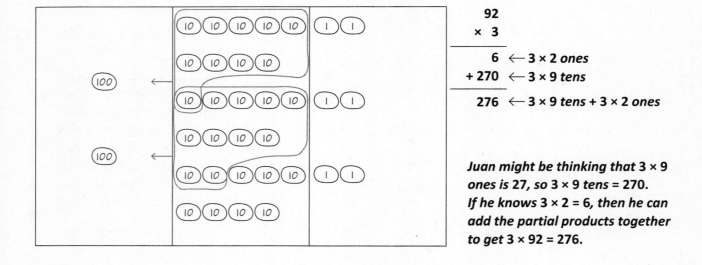

92
× 3

6 ← **3 × 2 ones**
+ 270 ← **3 × 9 tens**

276 ← **3 × 9 tens + 3 × 2 ones**

Juan might be thinking that 3 × 9 ones is 27, so 3 × 9 tens = 270. If he knows 3 × 2 = 6, then he can add the partial products together to get 3 × 92 = 276.

Lesson 20: Use concrete models to represent two-digit by one-digit multiplication.

3. Meg has 32 stamps. Ali has 4 times as many stickers as Meg. How many stamps does Ali have? Draw a strip diagram, use the place value chart to draw place value disks showing regrouping as necessary, and justify your response using partial products.

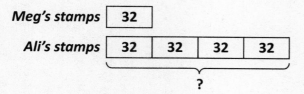

Meg's stamps | 32

Ali's stamps | 32 | 32 | 32 | 32

?

? = number of stamps Ali has

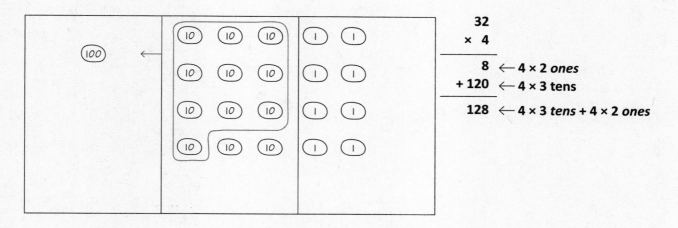

$$
\begin{array}{r}
32 \\
\times\ 4 \\
\hline
8 \quad \leftarrow \textbf{4 × 2 ones} \\
+\ 120 \quad \leftarrow \textbf{4 × 3 tens} \\
\hline
128 \quad \leftarrow \textbf{4 × 3 tens + 4 × 2 ones}
\end{array}
$$

Ali has 128 stamps.

Lesson 20:   Use concrete models to represent two-digit by one-digit multiplication.

83

Name _____   Date _____

1. Use your place value disks and charts to represent the following expressions. Record your work on the place value chart shown. Then record the partial products vertically. Problem (a) below is done for you.

   a. 3 × 22

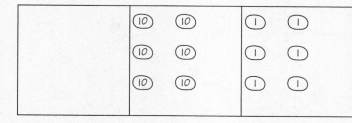

$$
\begin{array}{r}
2\,2 \\
\times\ 3 \\
\hline
6 \\
+60 \\
\hline
66
\end{array}
$$

6 ← 3 × 2 ones
+60 ← 3 × 2 tens
66 ← 3 × 2 tens + 3 × 2 ones

   b. 3 × 26

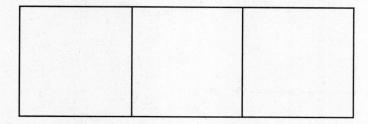

   c. 3 × 43

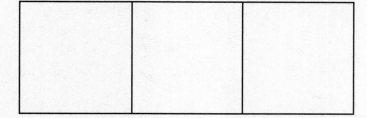

Lesson 20:   Use concrete models to represent two-digit by one-digit multiplication.

85

EUREKA
MATH
TEKS EDITION

d. 4 × 43

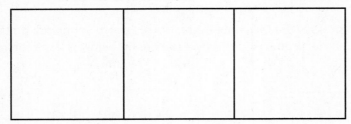

e. 4 × 65

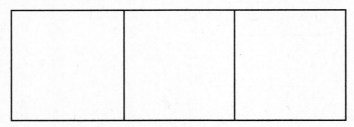

f. 4 × 54

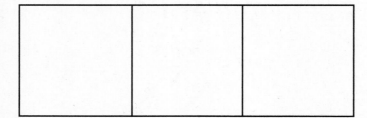

Lesson 20:   Use concrete models to represent two-digits by one-digit multiplication.

2. Anna says that knowing her multiplication facts helps her find products of larger numbers. She says that knowing that 3 × 8 = 24 and that 3 × 4 = 12 helps her find the product of 3 × 84. What do you think Anna means? Explain your thinking in words, and justify your response using partial products.

3. Mike has 41 stickers. Ruby has 3 times as many stickers as Mike. How many stickers does Ruby have? Draw a strip diagram, use the place value chart to draw place value disks, and justify your response using partial products.

EUREKA MATH
TEKS EDITION

Lesson 20: Use concrete models to represent two-digit by one-digit multiplication.

87

© Great Minds PBC TEKS Edition |
greatminds.org/Texas

1. Represent the expressions with dots. Write the problem vertically and record the partial products.

   a. 4 × 23

Hundreds	Tens	Ones
	• •	• • •
	• •	• • •
	• •	• • •
	• •	• • •
	•	

   ```
       23
   ×    4
   ─────────
       12   ← 4 × 3 ones
   +   80   ← 4 × 2 tens
   ─────────
       92   ← 4 × 2 tens + 4 × 3 ones
   ```

   > The place value chart shows the value of each digit. The dots show the number of each unit. I must show 4 groups of 2 tens and 3 ones. There will be more than 9 ones.

   b. 3 × 62

Hundreds	Tens	Ones
•	• • • • •	• •
	• • • • •	• •
	•	
	• • • • •	• •
	•	

   ```
       62
   ×    3
   ─────────
        6   ← 3 × 2 ones
   +  180   ← 3 × 6 tens
   ─────────
      186   ← 3 × 6 tens + 3 × 2 ones
   ```

   > I must show 3 groups of 6 tens and 2 ones. There will be more than 9 tens.

Lesson 21: Draw models to represent two-digit by one-digit multiplication.

89

EUREKA MATH
TEKS EDITION

© Great Minds PBC TEKS Edition |
greatminds.org/Texas

Name _____   Date _____

1. Represent the expressions with disks. Write the problem vertically and record the partial products.

a.   2 × 24

hundreds	tens	ones

$$
\begin{array}{r}
2\;4 \\
\times\;\;2 \\
\hline
8 \leftarrow 2 \times 4\ ones \\
+\;4\;0 \leftarrow 2 \times 2\ tens \\
\hline
4\;8 \leftarrow 2 \times 2\ tens + 2 \times 4\ ones
\end{array}
$$

b.   3 × 24

hundreds	tens	ones

Lesson 21:   Draw models to represent two-digit by one-digit multiplication.

91

EUREKA
MATH
TEKS EDITION

c. 4 × 24

hundreds	tens	ones

d. 5 × 24

hundreds	tens	ones

Lesson 21:   Draw models to represent two-digit by one-digit multiplication.

EUREKA
MATH
TEKS EDITION

2. Represent the expressions with disks. Write the problem vertically and record the partial products.

a. 5 × 23

hundreds	tens	ones

b. 5 × 32

hundreds	tens	ones

c. 3 × 64

hundreds	tens	ones

Lesson 21:   Draw models to represent two-digit by one-digit multiplication.

93

1. Solve using each method.

    2 × 45

No matter which method I choose to use I get the same product

When using the standard algorithm, I record the product all on one line.

I visualize my work with disks on the place value chart when I use the partial products method. I record each partial product on a separate line.

Partial Products	Standard Algorithm
45 × 2 ———— 10 ← 2 × 5 *ones* + 80 ← 2 × 4 *tens* ———— 90 ← 2 × 4 *tens* + 2 × 5 *ones*	45 × 2 ———— 90

2 times 5 ones equals 10 ones. I record 1 ten on the line in the tens place and 0 ones in the ones place of the product. 2 times 4 tens is 8 tens. I add the 1 ten on the line, which makes 9 tens. I cross out the 1 on the line in the tens place and write a 9 in the tens place of the product.

2. What is the product of 9 and 52?

When using the standard algorithm, I multiply the ones first.

52
× 9
————
468

9 times 2 ones equals 18 ones. I record 1 ten on the line in the tens place and 8 ones in the ones place of the product. 9 times 5 tens is 45 tens. I add the 1 ten on the line, which makes 46 tens. I cross out the 1 on the line in the tens place and write a 46 tens, which is the same as 4 hundreds and 6 tens in the hundreds and tens places of the product.

EUREKA MATH
TEKS EDITION

Lesson 22:   Multiply two-digit numbers by one-digit numbers using the standard algorithm.

95

© Great Minds PBC TEKS Edition |
greatminds.org/Texas

3. Joey earned 45 points playing a game. Joey's dad earned 4 times as many points as Joey. How many points did Joey's dad earn?

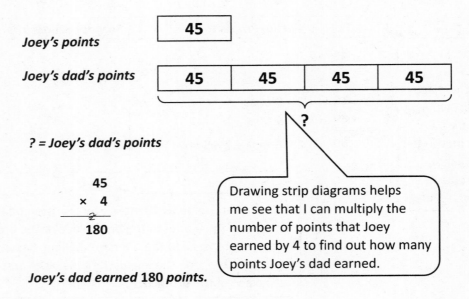

Joey's points | 45 |

Joey's dad's points | 45 | 45 | 45 | 45 |

?

? = Joey's dad's points

$$\begin{array}{r} 45 \\ \times\ 4 \\ \hline 2 \\ 180 \end{array}$$

Drawing strip diagrams helps me see that I can multiply the number of points that Joey earned by 4 to find out how many points Joey's dad earned.

Joey's dad earned 180 points.

Lesson 22:   Multiply two-digit numbers by one-digit numbers using the standard algorithm.

EUREKA
MATH
TEKS EDITION

Name _____ Date _____

1. Solve using each method.

Partial Products	Standard Algorithm	Partial Products	Standard Algorithm

a.   2 1
    ×   4
	2 1
	    × 4
		b. 5 6
		    × 3
			5 6
			    × 3

2. Solve using the standard algorithm.

a.   3 2
    ×   4
	b. 4 2
	    × 6
		c. 1 4
		    × 7

d.   4 4
    ×   3
	e. 5 7
	    × 8
		f. 8 4
		    × 9

Lesson 22:   Multiply two-digit numbers by one-digit numbers using the standard algorithm.

97

EUREKA MATH
TEKS EDITION

3. What is the product of 5 and 85?

4. Rowan earned 55 points playing a game. Rowan's mom earned 3 times as many points as Rowan. How many points did Rowan's mom earn?

5. To get enough money to go on a field trip, every student in a club has to raise $53 by selling chocolate bars. There are 9 students in the club. How much money does the club need to raise to go on the field trip?

Lesson 22:   Multiply two-digit numbers by one-digit numbers using the standard algorithm.

Jen makes 34 bracelets. She gives 19 bracelets away as gifts and sells the rest for $3 each. She would like to buy an art set that costs $55 with the money she earns. Does she have enough money to buy it? Explain why or why not.

> I can draw a model to show the known and unknown information. I can see from my drawing that I need to find a missing part. I can label my missing part with a ? to represent the number of bracelets Jen has left to sell.

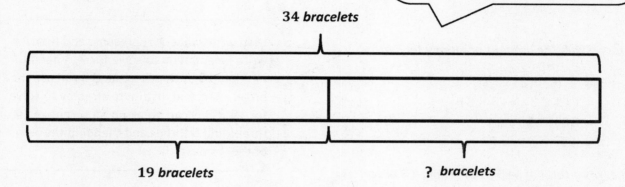

34 bracelets

19 bracelets   **? bracelets**

? represents the number of bracelets Jen has left to sell

$34 - 19 = ?$

$? = 15$

> I can write what ? represents and then write an equation to solve for ?. I subtract the given part, 19, from the whole amount, 34. I can use a compensation strategy to think of $34 - 19$ as $35 - 20$ because $35 - 20$ is an easier fact to solve. Jen has 15 bracelets left.

> This answer is reasonable because $19 + 15 = 34$. But it doesn't answer the question in the problem. Next, I have to figure out how much money Jen earns from selling the 15 bracelets, so I need to adjust my model.

EUREKA MATH®
TEKS EDITION

Lesson 23:   Solve two-step word problems involving multiplying single-digit factors by multiples of 10 and two-digit factors.

99

Now that I know Jen has 15 bracelets left, I can split this part into 15 smaller equal parts. I know that she sells each bracelet for $3, so each part has a value of $3. I can also label the unknown as m to represent how much money Jen earns in total.

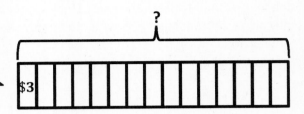

? *represents the amount of money Jen earns*

$15 \times 3 = \,?$

$\quad ? = (10 \times 3) + (5 \times 3)$

$\quad ? = 30 + 15$

$\quad ? = 45$

I can write what **?** represents and then write an equation to solve for **?**. I need to multiply 15 by 3, a large fact! I can use the break apart and distribute strategy to solve for 15×3. I can break up 15 threes as 10 threes and 5 threes and then find the sum of the 2 smaller facts.

Jen earns a total of $45 *from selling* 15 *bracelets.*

Jen does not have enough money to buy the art set. She is $10 *short.*

I am not finished answering the question until I explain why Jen does not have enough money to buy the art set.

Lesson 23:   Solve two-step word problems involving multiplying single-digit factors by multiples of 10 and two-digit factors.

EUREKA MATH®
TEKS EDITION

Name _____   Date _____

Use the RDW process for each problem.

1. There are 60 minutes in 1 hour. Use a strip diagram to find the total number of minutes in 6 hours and 15 minutes.

2. Ms. Lemus buys 7 boxes of snacks. Each box has 12 packets of fruit snacks and 20 packets of cashews. How many snack packets does she buy altogether?

3. Tamara wants to buy a tablet that costs $437. She saves $52 a month for 9 months. Does she have enough money to buy the tablet? Explain why or why not.

Lesson 23:   Solve two-step word problems involving multiplying single-digit factors by multiples of 10 and two-digit factors.

101

© Great Minds PBC TEKS Edition | greatminds.org/Texas

4. Mr. Ramirez receives 4 sets of books. Each set has 16 fiction books and 14 nonfiction books. He puts 97 books in his library and donates the rest. How many books does he donate?

5. Celia sells calendars for a fundraiser. Each calendar costs $9. She sells 16 calendars to her family members and 14 calendars to the people in her neighborhood. Her goal is to earn $300. Does Celia reach her goal? Explain your answer.

6. The video store sells science and history movies for $5 each. How much money does the video store make if it sells 33 science movies and 57 history movies?

Lesson 23:   Solve two-step word problems involving multiplying single-digit factors by multiples of 10 and two-digit factors.

EUREKA MATH
TEKS EDITION

Grade 3
Module 4

1. Use a ruler to measure the side lengths of the rectangle in centimeters. Mark each centimeter with a point, and draw lines from the points to show the square units. Then, count the squares you drew to find the total area.

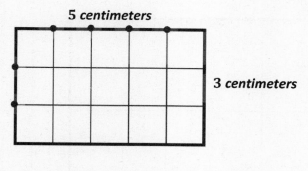

5 centimeters

3 centimeters

> I know the side length of a rectangle is the same as the number of centimeter tiles that make it. I also know that opposite sides of rectangles are equal, so I only need to measure 2 sides.

Total area: **15 square centimeters**

2. Each ☐ is 1 square centimeter. Sammy says that the side length of the rectangle below is 8 centimeters. Davis says the side length is 3 centimeters. Who is correct? Explain how you know.

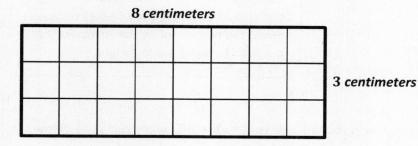

8 centimeters

3 centimeters

> An efficient strategy to find the area is to think of this rectangle as 3 rows of 8 tiles, or 3 eights. Then we can skip-count by eights 3 times to find the total number of square centimeter tiles.

They are both correct because I counted the tiles across the top, and there are 8 tiles, which means that the side length is 8 cm. Then I counted the tiles along the side, and there are 3 tiles, which means that the side length is 3 cm.

Lesson 1:   Relate side lengths to the number of tiles on a side.

105

EUREKA
MATH
TEKS EDITION

3. Shana uses square inch tiles to find the side lengths of the rectangle below. Label each side length. Then, find the total area.

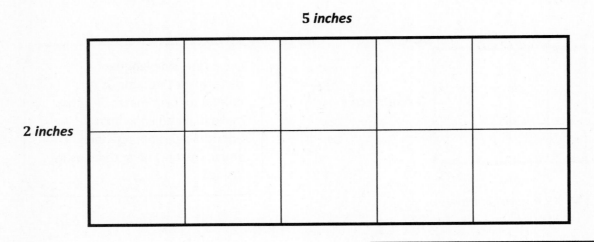

5 inches

2 inches

Total area: __10 *square inches*__

> I know the units are labeled differently for side lengths and area. I know the unit for side lengths is inches because the unit measures the length of the side in inches. For area, the unit is square inches because I count the number of square inch tiles that are used to make the rectangle.

4. How does knowing side lengths W and X help you find side lengths Y and Z on the rectangle below?

X

W Y

Z

I know that opposite sides of a rectangle are equal. So, if I know side length X, I also know side length Z. If I know side length W, I also know side length Y.

EUREKA MATH
TEKS EDITION

Name _____   Date _____

1. Ella placed square centimeter tiles on the rectangle below, and then labeled the side lengths. What is the area of her rectangle?

4 cm

2 cm

Total area: _____

2. Kyle uses square centimeter tiles to find the side lengths of the rectangle below. Label each side length. Then, count the tiles to find the total area.

Total area: _____

3. Maura uses square inch tiles to find the side lengths of the rectangle below. Label each side length. Then, find the total area.

Total area: _____

Lesson 1:   Relate side lengths to the number of tiles on a side.

107

4. Each square unit below is 1 square inch. Claire says that the side length of the rectangle below is 3 inches. Tyler says the side length is 5 inches. Who is correct? Explain how you know.

5. Label the unknown side lengths for the rectangle below, and then find the area. Explain how you used the lengths provided to find the unknown lengths and area.

4 inches

2 inches

_____

_____

Total area: _____

Lesson 1:   Relate side lengths to the number of tiles on a side.

1. Use the centimeter side of a ruler to draw in the tiles. Then, find and label the unknown side length. Skip-count the tiles to check your work. Write a multiplication sentence for each tiled rectangle.

   a. Area: 12 square centimeters

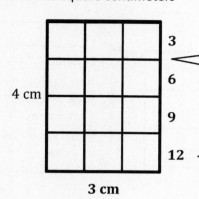

3
6
9
12

4 cm

3 cm

I can use my ruler to mark each centimeter. Then, I can connect the marks to draw the tiles. I'll count the square units and label the unknown side length 3 cm.

Next, I'll skip-count by 3 to check that the total number of tiles matches the given area of 12 square centimeters.

____4____ × ____3____ = ____12____

I can write 3 for the unknown factor because my tiled array shows 4 rows of 3 tiles.

   b. Area: 12 square centimeters

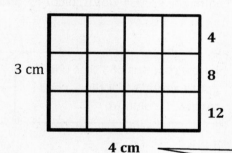

4
8
12

3 cm

4 cm

____3____ × ____4____ = ____12____

After I use my ruler to draw the tiles, I can count to find the unknown side length and label it.

I can write the number sentence 3 × 4 = 12 because there are 3 rows of 4 tiles, which is a total of 12 tiles.

The area of the rectangles in parts (a) and (b) is 12 square centimeters. That means both rectangles have the same area even though they look different.

2. Ella makes a rectangle with 24 square centimeter tiles. There are 4 equal rows of tiles.

a. How many tiles are in each row? Use words, pictures, and numbers to support your answer.

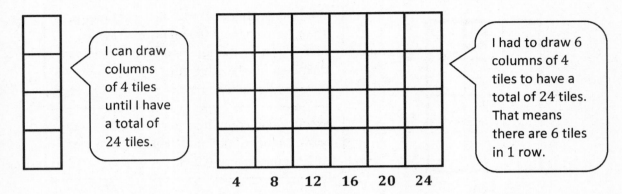

There are 6 tiles in each row. I drew columns of 4 tiles until I had a total of 24 tiles. Then I counted how many tiles are in 1 row. I could also find the answer by thinking about the problem as $4 \times$ _____ $= 24$ because I know that $4 \times 6 = 24$.

b. Can Ella arrange all of her 24 square centimeter tiles into 3 equal rows? Use words, pictures, and numbers to support your answer.

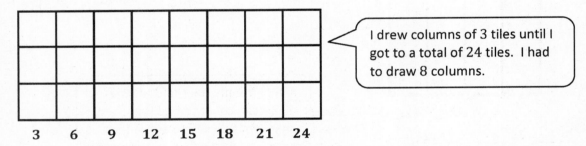

Yes, Ella can arrange all of her 24 tiles into 3 equal rows. I drew columns of 3 tiles until I had a total of 24 tiles. I can use my picture to see that there are 8 tiles in each row. I can also use multiplication to help me because I know that $3 \times 8 = 24$.

c. Do the rectangles in parts (a) and (b) have the same total area? Explain how you know.

Yes, the rectangles in parts (a) and (b) have the same area because they are both made up of 24 square centimeter tiles. The rectangles look different because they have different side lengths, but they have the same area.

This is different than Problem 1 because the rectangles in Problem 1 had the same side lengths. They were just rotated.

Lesson 2:   Form rectangles by tiling with unit squares to make arrays.

Name _____   Date _____

1. Use the centimeter side of a ruler to draw in the tiles. Find the unknown side length or skip-count to find the unknown area. Then, complete the multiplication equations.

a. Area: **24** square centimeters.

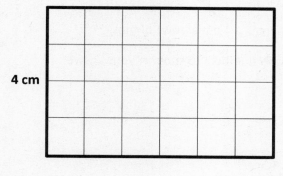

4 cm

___4___ × _____ = ___24___

b. Area: **24** square centimeters.

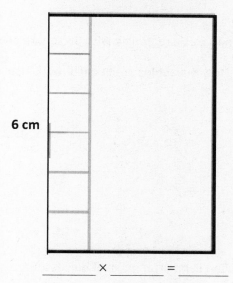

6 cm

_____ × _____ = _____

c. Area: **15** square centimeters.

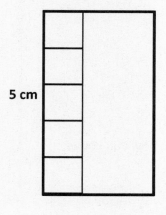

5 cm

_____ × _____ = _____

d. Area: **15** square centimeters.

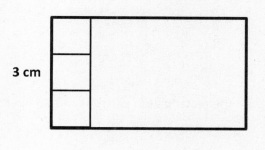

3 cm

_____ × _____ = _____

Lesson 2:   Form rectangles by tiling with unit squares to make arrays.

111

2. Ally makes a rectangle with 45 square inch tiles. She arranges the tiles in 5 equal rows. How many square inch tiles are in each row? Use words, pictures, and numbers to support your answer.

3. Leon makes a rectangle with 36 square centimeter tiles. There are 4 equal rows of tiles.

   a. How many tiles are in each row? Use words, pictures, and numbers to support your answer.

   b. Can Leon arrange all of his 36 square centimeter tiles into 6 equal rows? Use words, pictures, and numbers to support your answer.

   c. Do the rectangles in Parts (a) and (b) have the same total area? Explain how you know.

Lesson 2:   Form rectangles by tiling with unit squares to make arrays.

1. Each ☐ represents 1 square centimeter. Draw to find the number of rows and columns in each array. Match it to its completed array. Then, fill in the blanks to make a true equation to find each array's area.

a.

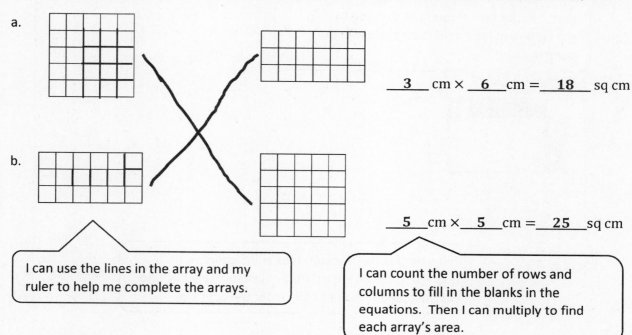

___3___ cm × ___6___ cm = ___18___ sq cm

b.

___5___ cm × ___5___ cm = ___25___ sq cm

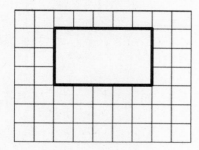

I can use the lines in the array and my ruler to help me complete the arrays.

I can count the number of rows and columns to fill in the blanks in the equations. Then I can multiply to find each array's area.

2. A painting covers the tile wall in Ava's kitchen, as shown below.

a. Ava skip-counts by 9 to find the total number of square tiles on the wall. She says there are 63 square tiles. Is she correct? Explain your answer.

Yes, Ava is correct. Even though I can't see all of the tiles, I can use the first row and column to see that there are 7 rows of 9 tiles. I can multiply 7×9, which equals 63.

EUREKA
MATH
TEKS EDITION

Lesson 3:   Draw rows and columns to determine the area of a rectangle given an incomplete array.

113

© Great Minds PBC TEKS Edition | greatminds.org/Texas

b. How many square tiles are under the painting?

> I can use the tiles around the painting to help me figure out how many tiles are under the painting.

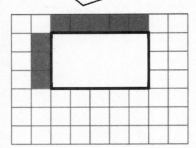

$3 \times 5 = 15$

> There are 3 rows of square tiles and 5 columns of square tiles under the painting. I can multiply 3×5 to find the total number of tiles under the painting.

$63 - 48 = 15$

> I know from part (a) that there are 63 total tiles. So, I could also solve by subtracting the number of tiles that I can see from the total.

There are 15 square tiles under the painting.

Lesson 3:   Draw rows and columns to determine the area of a rectangle given an incomplete array.

EUREKA
MATH
TEKS EDITION

Name _____   Date _____

1. Each ☐ represents 1 square centimeter. Draw to find the number of rows and columns in each array.
    Match it to its completed array. Then, fill in the blanks to make a true equation to find each array's area.

a.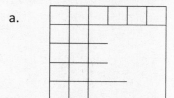

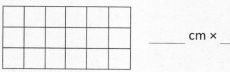   _____ cm × _____ cm = _____ sq cm

b.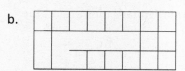

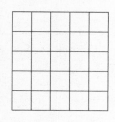   _____ cm × _____ cm = _____ sq cm

c.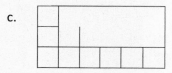

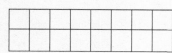   _____ cm × _____ cm = _____ sq cm

    _____ cm × _____ cm = _____ sq cm

d.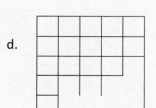

e.

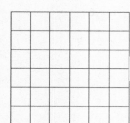   _____ cm × _____ cm = _____ sq cm

f.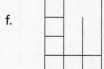

   _____ cm × _____ cm = _____ sq cm

Lesson 3:   Draw rows and columns to determine the area of a rectangle given an
incomplete array.

© Great Minds PBC TEKS Edition |
greatminds.org/Texas

115

2. Minh skip-counts by sixes to find the total square units in the rectangle below. She says there are 36 square units. Is she correct? Explain your answer.

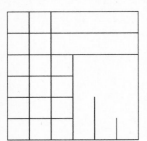

3. The tub in Paige's bathroom covers the tile floor as shown below. How many square tiles are on the floor, including the tiles under the tub?

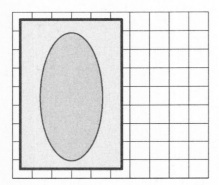

4. Frank sees a notebook on top of his chessboard. How many squares are covered by the notebook? Explain your answer.

Lesson 3:   Draw rows and columns to determine the area of a rectangle given an
                   incomplete array.

EUREKA
MATH
TEKS EDITION

1. Find the area of the rectangular array. Label the side lengths of the matching area model, and write a multiplication equation for the area model.

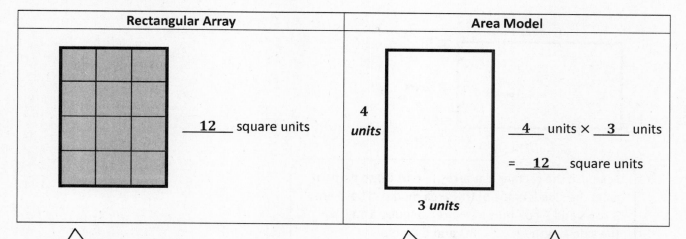

Rectangular Array	Area Model

____12____ square units

4 units

3 units

___4___ units × ___3___ units

= ___12___ square units

I can skip-count rows by 3 or columns by 4 to find the area of the rectangular array.

I can use the rectangular array to help me label the side lengths of the area model. There are 4 rows, so the width is 4 units. There are 3 columns, so the length is 3 units.

I can multiply 4 × 3 to find the area. The area model and the rectangular array have the same area of 12 square units.

2. Mason arranges square pattern blocks into a 3 by 6 array. Draw Mason's array on the the grid below. How many square units are in Mason's rectangular array?

a.

There are 18 square units in Mason's rectangular array.

I can draw a rectangular array with 3 rows and 6 columns. Then I can multiply 3 × 6 to find the total number of square units in the rectangular array.

b. Label the side lengths of Mason's array from part (a) on the rectangle below. Then, write a multiplication sentence to represent the area of the rectangle.

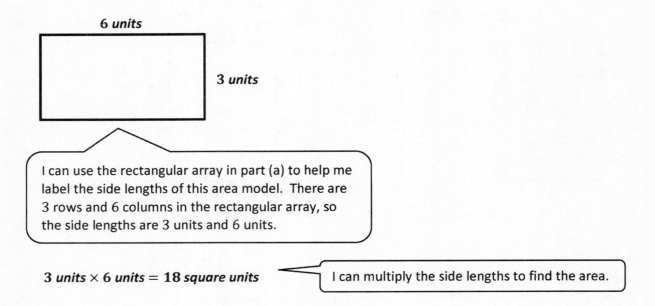

6 units

3 units

I can use the rectangular array in part (a) to help me label the side lengths of this area model. There are 3 rows and 6 columns in the rectangular array, so the side lengths are 3 units and 6 units.

3 units × 6 units = 18 square units

I can multiply the side lengths to find the area.

3. Luke draws a rectangle that is 4 square feet. Savannah draws a rectangle that is 4 square inches. Whose rectangle is larger in area? How do you know?

Luke's rectangle is larger in area because they both used the same number of units, but the size of the units is different. Luke used square feet, which are larger than square inches. Since the units that Luke used are larger than the units that Savannah used and they both used the same number of units, Luke's rectangle is larger in area.

I can think about the lesson today to help me answer this question. My partner and I made rectangles using square inch and square centimeter tiles. We both used the same number of tiles to make our rectangles, but we noticed that the rectangle made of square inches was larger in area than the rectangle made of square centimeters. The larger unit, square inches, made a rectangle with a larger area.

Lesson 4:   Interpret area models to form rectangular arrays.

EUREKA MATH
TEKS EDITION

Name _____   Date _____

1. Find the area of each rectangular array. Label the side lengths of the matching area model, and write a multiplication equation for each area model.

Rectangular Arrays	Area Models
a. _____ square units	3 units _____ 2 units 3 units × _____ units = _____ square units
b. _____ square units	_____ units × _____ units = _____ square units
c. _____ square units	_____ units × _____ units = _____ square units
d. _____ square units	_____ units × _____ units = _____ square units

EUREKA MATH®
TEKS EDITION

© Great Minds PBC TEKS Edition |
greatminds.org/Texas

2. Jillian arranges square pattern blocks into a 7 by 4 array. Draw Jillian's array on the the grid below. How many square units are in Jillian's rectangular array?

a.

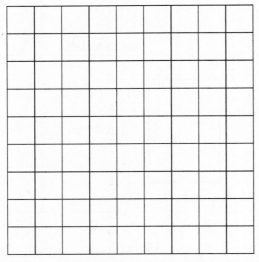

b. Label the side lengths of Jillian's array from Part (a) on the rectangle below. Then, write a multiplication sentence to represent the area of the rectangle.

3. Fiona draws a 24 square centimeter rectangle. Gregory draws a 24 square inch rectangle. Whose rectangle is larger in area? How do you know?

Lesson 4:   Interpret area models to form rectangular arrays.

EUREKA
MATH
TEKS EDITION

1. Write a multiplication equation to find the area of the rectangle.

8 cm

4 cm   Area: ___**32**___ sq cm

I know that I can multiply the side lengths, 4 and 8, to find the area.

___**4**___ × ___**8**___ = ___**32**___

2. Write a multiplication equation and a division equation to find the unknown side length for the rectangle.

___**9**___ ft

2 ft   Area: 18 sq ft

To solve, I can think of this as multiplication with an unknown factor, $2 \times$ ____ $= 18$. Or, I can divide the area by the known side length, $18 \div 2 =$ ____. Either way, the answer is 9.

___**2**___ × ___**9**___ = ___**18**___

___**18**___ ÷ ___**2**___ = ___**9**___

3. On the grid below, draw a rectangle that has an area of 24 square units. Label the side lengths.

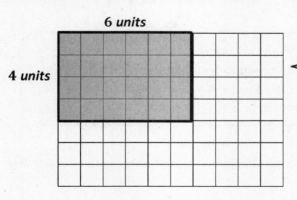

6 units

4 units

To draw a rectangle with an area of 24 square units, I can think about factors of 24. I know $4 \times 6 = 24$, so my side lengths can be 4 and 6.

Lesson 5:   Find the area of a rectangle through multiplication of the side lengths.

121

EUREKA
MATH
TEKS EDITION

4. Keith draws a rectangle that has side lengths of 6 inches and 3 inches. What is the area of the rectangle? Explain how you found your answer.

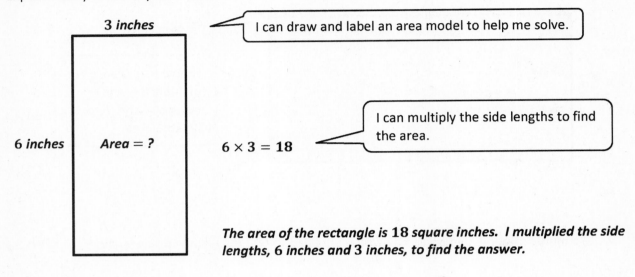

The area of the rectangle is 18 square inches. I multiplied the side lengths, 6 inches and 3 inches, to find the answer.

5. Isabelle draws a rectangle with a side length of 5 centimeters and an area of 30 square centimeters. What is the other side length? How do you know?

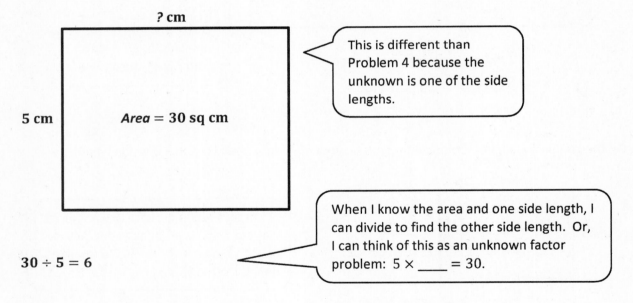

The other side length is 6 centimeters. I divided the area, 30 square centimeters, by the known side length, 5 centimeters, and 30 ÷ 5 = 6.

Lesson 5:   Find the area of a rectangle through multiplication of the side lengths.

EUREKA MATH
TEKS EDITION

Name _____   Date _____

1. Write a multiplication equation to find the area of each rectangle.

a.

8 cm

3 cm | Area: _____ sq cm

_____ × _____ = _____

b.

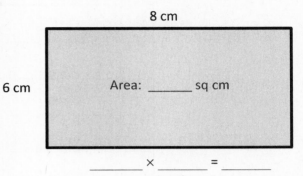

8 cm

6 cm   Area: _____ sq cm

_____ × _____ = _____

c.

4 ft

4 ft | Area: _____ sq ft

_____ × _____ = _____

d.

7 ft

4 ft   Area: _____ sq ft

_____ × _____ = _____

2. Write a multiplication equation and a division equation to find the unknown side length for each rectangle.

a.

_____ ft.

3 ft | Area: 24 sq ft

_____ × _____ = _____

_____ ÷ _____ = _____

b.

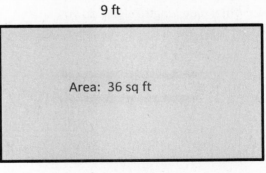

9 ft

_____ ft   Area: 36 sq ft

_____ × _____ = _____

_____ ÷ _____ = _____

Lesson 5: Find the area of a rectangle through multiplication of the side lengths.

123

EUREKA MATH
TEKS EDITION

3. On the grid below, draw a rectangle that has an area of 32 square centimeters. Label the side lengths.

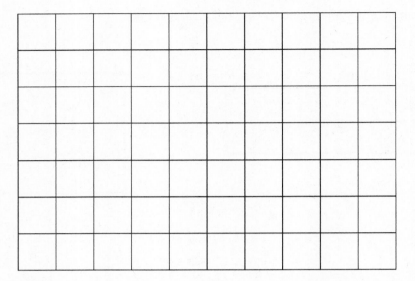

4. Patricia draws a rectangle that has side lengths of 4 centimeters and 9 centimeters. What is the area of the rectangle? Explain how you found your answer.

5. Charles draws a rectangle with a side length of 9 inches and an area of 27 square inches. What is the other side length? How do you know?

Lesson 5:   Find the area of a rectangle through multiplication of the side lengths.

1. Use the grid to answer the questions below.

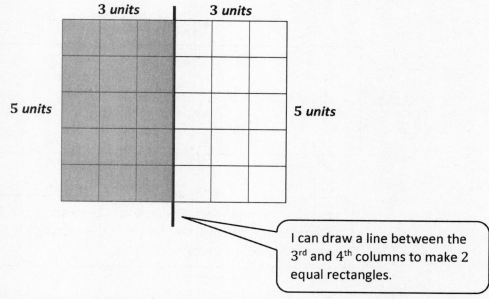

3 units   3 units

5 units   5 units

I can draw a line between the 3rd and 4th columns to make 2 equal rectangles.

a. Draw a line to divide the grid into 2 equal rectangles. Shade in 1 of the rectangles that you created.

I can count the units on each side to help me label the side lengths of each rectangle.

b. Label the side lengths of each rectangle.

c. Write an equation to show the total area of the 2 rectangles.

$$Area = (5 \times 3) + (5 \times 3)$$
$$= 15 + 15$$
$$= 30$$

The total area is 30 square units.

I can find the area of each smaller rectangle by multiplying 5×3. Then, I can add the areas of the 2 equal rectangles to find the total area.

EUREKA MATH
TEKS EDITION

Lesson 6:   Analyze different rectangles and reason about their area.

125

© Great Minds PBC TEKS Edition |
greatminds.org/Texas

2. Phoebe cuts out the 2 equal rectangles from Problem 1(a) and puts the two shorter sides together.

a. Draw Phoebe's new rectangle, and label the side lengths below.

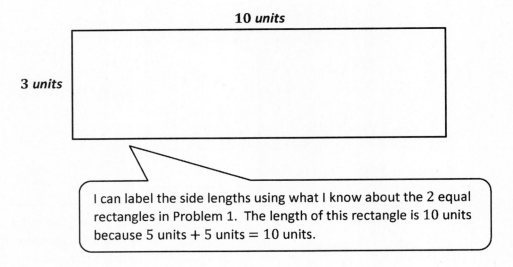

10 units

3 units

I can label the side lengths using what I know about the 2 equal rectangles in Problem 1. The length of this rectangle is 10 units because 5 units + 5 units = 10 units.

b. Find the total area of the new, longer rectangle.

$Area = 3 \times 10$
$= 30$
The total area is **30** square units.

I can find the area by multiplying the side lengths.

c. Is the area of the new, longer rectangle equal to the total area in Problem 1(c)? Explain why or why not.

Yes, the area of the new, longer rectangle is equal to the total area in Problem 1(c). Phoebe just rearranged the 2 smaller, equal rectangles, so the total area didn't change.

I know that the total area doesn't change just because the 2 equal rectangles were moved around to form a new, longer rectangle. No units were taken away and none were added, so the area stays the same.

Lesson 6:   Analyze different rectangles and reason about their area.

EUREKA
MATH
TEKS EDITION

Name _____   Date _____

1. Use the grid to answer the questions below.

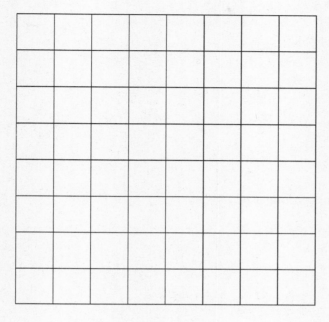

a. Draw a line to divide the grid into 2 equal rectangles. Shade in 1 of the rectangles that you created.

b. Label the side lengths of each rectangle.

c. Write an equation to show the total area of the 2 rectangles.

EUREKA
MATH
TEKS EDITION

Lesson 6:   Analyze different rectangles and reason about their area.

127

© Great Minds PBC TEKS Edition |
greatminds.org/Texas

2. Alexa cuts out the 2 equal rectangles from Problem 1(a) and puts the two shorter sides together.

   a. Draw Alexa's new rectangle and label the side lengths below.

   b. Find the total area of the new, longer rectangle.

   c. Is the area of the new, longer rectangle equal to the total area in Problem 1(c)?
       Explain why or why not.

Lesson 6:   Analyze different rectangles and reason about their area.

1. Label the side lengths of the shaded and unshaded rectangles. Then, find the total area of the large rectangle by adding the areas of the 2 smaller rectangles.

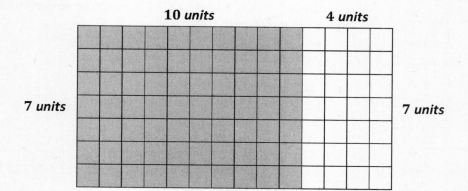

10 *units*   **4** *units*

7 *units*   **7** *units*

$7 \times 14 = 7 \times ($ __**10**__ $+$ __**4**__ $)$

$= (7 \times$ __**10**__ $) + (7 \times$ __**4**__ $)$

$=$ __**70**__ $+$ __**28**__

$=$ __**98**__

Area: __**98**__ square units

I can count the units on each side to help me label the side lengths of each rectangle.

EUREKA
MATH
TEKS EDITION

Lesson 7:   Apply the distributive property as a strategy to find the total area of a larger rectangle by adding two products.

129

© Great Minds PBC TEKS Edition |
greatminds.org/Texas

2. Vickie imagines 1 more row of seven to find the total area of a 9×7 rectangle. Explain how this could help her solve 9×7.

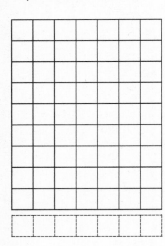

This can help her solve 9×7 because now she can think of it as 10×7 minus 1 seven. 10×7 might be easier for Vickie to solve than 9×7.

$$10 \times 7 = 70$$

$$70 - 7 = 63$$

This reminds me of the $9 = 10 - 1$ strategy that I can use to multiply by 9.

3. Break the 16×6 rectangle into 2 rectangles by shading one smaller rectangle within it. Then, find the total area by finding the sum of the areas of the 2 smaller rectangles. Explain your thinking.

6 units

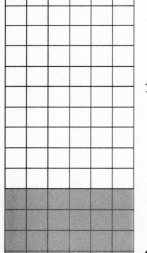

10 units

6 units

Area $= (10 \times 6) + (6 \times 6)$
  $= 60 + 36$
  $= 96$

The total area is 96 square units.

I broke apart the 16×6 rectangle into 2 smaller rectangles: 10×6 and 6×6. I chose to break it apart like this because those are easy facts for me. I multiplied the side lengths to find the area of each smaller rectangle and added those areas to find the total area.

I can break apart the rectangle any way I want to, but I like to look for facts that are easy for me to solve. Multiplying by 10 is easy for me. I also could have broken it apart into 8×6 and 8×6. Then I would really only have to solve one fact.

Lesson 7:   Apply the distributive property as a strategy to find the total area of a larger rectangle by adding two products.

EUREKA
MATH®
TEKS EDITION

Name _____   Date _____

1. Label the side lengths of the shaded and unshaded rectangles. Then, find the total area of the large rectangle by adding the areas of the 2 smaller rectangles.

a.

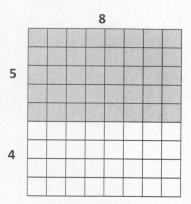

$9 \times 8 = (5+4) \times 8$

$= (5 \times 8) + (4 \times 8)$

$= \underline{\hspace{1cm}} + \underline{\hspace{1cm}}$

$= \underline{\hspace{1cm}}$

Area: _____ square units

b.

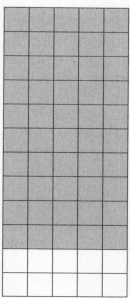

$12 \times 5 = (\underline{\hspace{1cm}} + 2) \times 5$

$= (\underline{\hspace{1cm}} \times 5) + (2 \times 5)$

$= \underline{\hspace{1cm}} + 10$

$= \underline{\hspace{1cm}}$

Area: _____ square units

c.

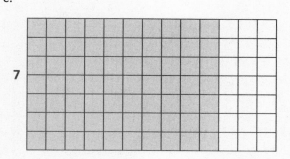

$7 \times 13 = 7 \times (\underline{\hspace{1cm}} + 3)$

$= (7 \times \underline{\hspace{1cm}}) + (7 \times 3)$

$= \underline{\hspace{1cm}} + \underline{\hspace{1cm}}$

$= \underline{\hspace{1cm}}$

Area: _____ square units

d.

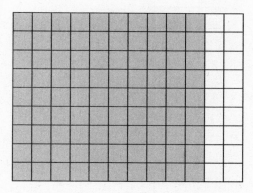

$9 \times 12 = 9 \times (\underline{\hspace{1cm}} + \underline{\hspace{1cm}})$

$= (9 \times \underline{\hspace{1cm}}) + (9 \times \underline{\hspace{1cm}})$

$= \underline{\hspace{1cm}} + \underline{\hspace{1cm}}$

$= \underline{\hspace{1cm}}$

Area: _____ square units

EUREKA MATH
TEKS EDITION

Lesson 7:   Apply the distributive property as a strategy to find the total area of a larger rectangle by adding two products.

131

© Great Minds PBC TEKS Edition | greatminds.org/Texas

2. Finn imagines 1 more row of nine to find the total area of 9 × 9 rectangle. Explain how this could help him solve 9 × 9.

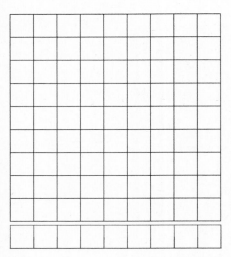

3. Shade an area to break the 16 × 4 rectangle into 2 smaller rectangles. Then, find the sum of the areas of the 2 smaller rectangles to find the total area. Explain your thinking.

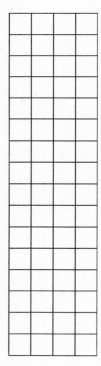

Lesson 7:   Apply the distributive property as a strategy to find the total area of a larger rectangle by adding two products.

EUREKA
MATH
TEKS EDITION

1. The rectangles below have the same area. Move the parentheses to find the unknown side lengths.
    Then, solve.

    a.

    6 cm

    4 cm

    b.

    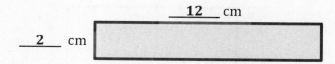

    ___12___ cm

    ___2___ cm

    Area: $4 \times$ ___6___ $=$ ___24___

    Area: ___24___ sq cm

    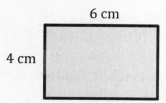

    I can
    multiply
    the side
    lengths to
    find the
    area.

    Area: $4 \times 6 = (2 \times 2) \times 6$
    $= 2 \times (2 \times 6)$
    $= $ ___2___ $\times$ ___12___
    $= $ ___24___

    Area: ___24___ sq cm

    I can move the parentheses to be
    around 2×6. After I multiply 2×6,
    I have new side lengths of 2 cm and
    12 cm. I can label the side lengths
    on the rectangle. The area didn't
    change; it's still 24 sq cm.

2. Does Problem 1 show all the possible whole number side lengths for a rectangle with an area of 24
    square centimeters? How do you know?

    *No, Problem 1 doesn't show all possible whole number side lengths. I check by trying to multiply each
    number 1 through 10 by another number to equal 24. If I can find numbers that make 24 when I
    multiply them, then I know those are possible side lengths.*

    *I know $1 \times 24 = 24$. So 1 cm and 24 cm are possible side lengths. I already have a multiplication
    fact for 2, 2×12. I know $3 \times 8 = 24$, which means $8 \times 3 = 24$. I already have a multiplication fact
    for 4, 4×6. That also means that I have a fact for 6, $6 \times 4 = 24$. I know there's not a whole number
    that can be multiplied by 5, 7, 9, or 10 that equals 24. So besides the side lengths from Problem 1,
    other ones could be 1 cm and 24 cm or 8 cm and 3 cm.*

    I know that I can't have side lengths that are both two-digit numbers because
    when I multiply 2 two-digit numbers, the product is much larger than 24.

EUREKA
MATH
TEKS EDITION

Lesson 8:   Demonstrate the possible whole number side lengths of rectangles
with areas of 24, 36, 48, or 72 square units using the associative
property.

© Great Minds PBC TEKS Edition |
greatminds.org/Texas

133

3. a. Find the area of the rectangle below.

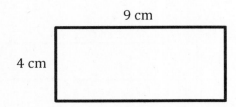

9 cm

4 cm

Area = 4×9

= 36

The area of the rectangle is 36 square centimeters.

a. Marcus says a 2 cm by 18 cm rectangle has the same area as the rectangle in part (a). Place parentheses in the equation to find the related fact and solve. Is Marcus correct? Why or why not?

$2 \times 18 = 2 \times (2 \times 9)$

$= (2 \times 2) \times 9$

$= \underline{\quad 4 \quad} \times \underline{\quad 9 \quad}$

$= \underline{\quad 36 \quad}$

Area: $\underline{\quad 36 \quad}$ sq cm

Yes, Marcus is correct because I can rewrite **18** *as* 2×9. *Then I can move the parentheses so they are around* 2×2. *After I multiply* 2×2, *I have* **4** cm *and* **9** cm *as side lengths, just like in part (a).*

$2 \times 18 = 4 \times 9 = 36$

Even though the rectangles in parts (a) and (b) have different side lengths, the areas are the same. Rewriting 18 as 2×9 and moving the parentheses helps me to see that $2 \times 18 = 4 \times 9$.

b. Use the expression 4×9 to find different side lengths for a rectangle that has the same area as the rectangle in part (a). Show your equations using parentheses. Then, estimate to draw the rectangle and label the side lengths.

$4 \times 9 = 4 \times (3 \times 3)$

$= (4 \times 3) \times 3$

$= 12 \times 3$

$= 36$

Area: **36 sq cm**

I can rewrite 9 as 3×3. Then I can move the parentheses and multiply to find the new side lengths, 12 cm and 3 cm. I can estimate to draw the new rectangle. If I need to, I can use repeated addition, $12 + 12 + 12$, to double check that $12 \times 3 = 36$.

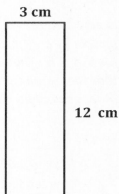

3 cm

12 cm

Lesson 8: Demonstrate the possible whole number side lengths of rectangles with areas of 24, 36, 48, or 72 square units using the associative property.

© Great Minds PBC TEKS Edition | greatminds.org/Texas

EUREKA MATH®
TEKS EDITION

Name _____ Date _____

1. The rectangles below have the same area. Move the parentheses to find the unknown side lengths. Then, solve.

36 cm

1 cm

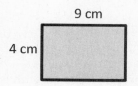

9 cm

4 cm

b. Area: 1 × 36 = _____

Area: _____ sq cm

a. Area: 4 × _____ = _____

Area: _____ sq cm

_____ cm

2 cm

c. Area: 4 × 9 = (2 × 2) × 9

= 2 × 2 × 9

= _____ × _____

= _____

Area: _____ sq cm

_____ cm

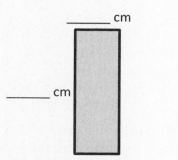

_____ cm

d. Area: 4 × 9 = 4 × (3 × 3)

= 4 × 3 × 3

= _____ × _____

= _____

Area: _____ sq cm

e. Area: 12 × 3 = (6 × 2) × 3

= 6 × 2 × 3

_____ cm

= _____ × _____

= _____

_____ cm

Area: _____ sq cm

2. Does Problem 1 show all the possible whole number side lengths for a rectangle with an area of 36 square centimeters? How do you know?

3. a. Find the area of the rectangle below.

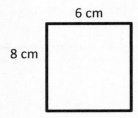

6 cm

8 cm

b. Hilda says a 4 cm by 12 cm rectangle has the same area as the rectangle in Part (a). Place parentheses in the equation to find the related fact and solve. Is Hilda correct? Why or why not?

$4 \times 12 = 4 \times 2 \times 6$

$= 4 \times 2 \times 6$

$= \underline{\hspace{1cm}} \times \underline{\hspace{1cm}}$

$= \underline{\hspace{1cm}}$

Area: _____ sq cm

c. Use the expression 8×6 to find different side lengths for a rectangle that has the same area as the rectangle in Part (a). Show your equations using parentheses. Then, estimate to draw the rectangle and label the side lengths.

Lesson 8:   Demonstrate the possible whole number side lengths of rectangles with areas of 24, 36, 48, or 72 square units using the associative property.

© Great Minds PBC TEKS Edition | greatminds.org/Texas

EUREKA MATH
TEKS EDITION

1. Molly draws a square with sides that are 8 inches long. What is the area of the square?

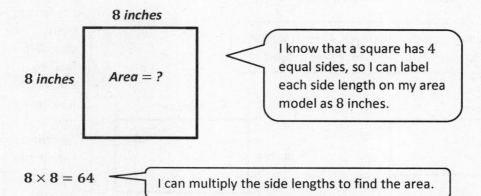

8 inches

8 inches   *Area = ?*

I know that a square has 4 equal sides, so I can label each side length on my area model as 8 inches.

$8 \times 8 = 64$

I can multiply the side lengths to find the area.

The area of the square is 64 square inches.

2. Each ⬜ is 1 square unit. Nathan uses the same square units to draw a 2×8 rectangle and says that it has the same area as the rectangle below. Is he correct? Explain why or why not.

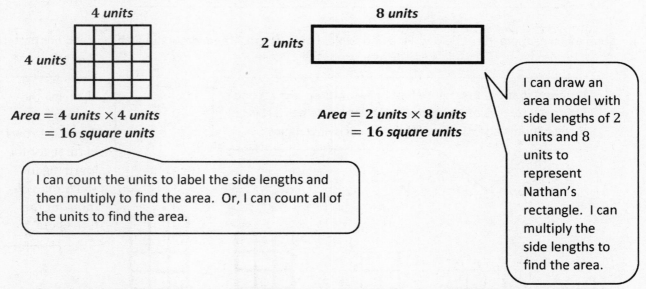

4 units

4 units

8 units

2 units

Area = 4 units × 4 units
= 16 square units

Area = 2 units × 8 units
= 16 square units

I can count the units to label the side lengths and then multiply to find the area. Or, I can count all of the units to find the area.

I can draw an area model with side lengths of 2 units and 8 units to represent Nathan's rectangle. I can multiply the side lengths to find the area.

Yes, Nathan is correct. Both rectangles have the same area, 16 square units. The rectangles have different side lengths, but when you multiply the side lengths, you get the same area.

$$4 \times 4 = 2 \times 8 = 16$$

EUREKA
MATH
TEKS EDITION

Lesson 9:   Solve word problems involving area.

3. A rectangular notepad has a total area of 24 square inches. Draw and label two possible notepads with different side lengths, each having an area of 24 square inches.

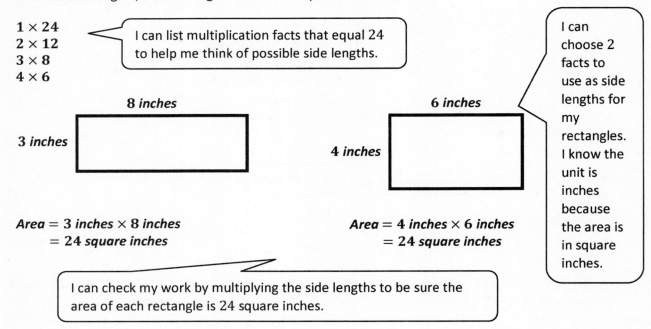

1×24
2×12
3×8
4×6

I can list multiplication facts that equal 24 to help me think of possible side lengths.

8 inches

3 inches

I can choose 2 facts to use as side lengths for my rectangles. I know the unit is inches because the area is in square inches.

6 inches

4 inches

Area = 3 inches × 8 inches
      = 24 square inches

Area = 4 inches × 6 inches
      = 24 square inches

I can check my work by multiplying the side lengths to be sure the area of each rectangle is 24 square inches.

4. Sophia makes the pattern below. Find and explain her pattern. Then, draw the fifth figure in her pattern.

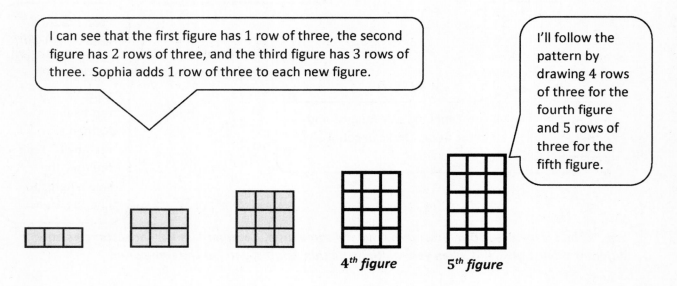

I can see that the first figure has 1 row of three, the second figure has 2 rows of three, and the third figure has 3 rows of three. Sophia adds 1 row of three to each new figure.

I'll follow the pattern by drawing 4 rows of three for the fourth figure and 5 rows of three for the fifth figure.

4ᵗʰ figure

5ᵗʰ figure

Sophia adds 1 row of three to each figure. The fifth figure has 5 rows of three.

Lesson 9:   Solve word problems involving area.

EUREKA MATH
TEKS EDITION

Name _____   Date _____

1. A square calendar has sides that are 9 inches long. What is the calendar's area?

2. Each 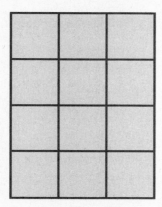 is 1 square unit. Sienna uses the same square units to draw a 6 × 2 rectangle and says that it has the same area as the rectangle below. Is she correct? Explain why or why not.

3. The surface of an office desk has an area of 15 square feet. Its length is 5 feet. How wide is the office desk?

EUREKA MATH
TEKS EDITION

Lesson 9:   Solve word problems involving area.

139

© Great Minds PBC TEKS Edition |
greatminds.org/Texas

4. A rectangular garden has a total area of 48 square yards. Draw and label two possible rectangular gardens with different side lengths that have the same area.

5. Lila makes the pattern below. Find and explain her pattern. Then, draw the *fifth* figure in her pattern.

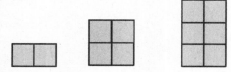

Lesson 9:   Solve word problems involving area.

EUREKA
MATH®
TEKS EDITION

1. The shaded figure below is made up of 2 rectangles. Find the total area of the shaded figure.

8 units

B

2 units

6 units

A

> I can count the square units and label the side lengths of each rectangle inside the figure.

4 units

$6 \times 4 = 24$ $2 \times 8 = 16$

> I can multiply the side lengths to find the area of each rectangle inside the figure.

***Area of A:* 24 sq units**   ***Area of B:* 16 sq units**

> I can add the areas of the rectangles to find the total area of the figure.

Area of A + Area of B = ____24____ sq units + ____16____ sq units = ____40____ sq units

6   10

$24 + 6 = 30$

$30 + 10 = 40$

> I can use a number bond to help me make a ten to add. I can decompose 16 into 6 and 10. $24 + 6 = 30$ and $30 + 10 = 40$. The area of the figure is 40 square units.

Lesson 10:   Find areas by decomposing into rectangles or completing composite figures to form rectangles.

2. The figure shows a small rectangle cut out of a big rectangle. Find the area of the shaded figure.

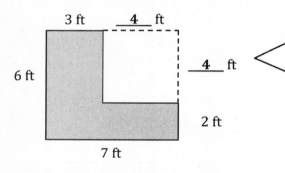

9 cm

9 cm   5 cm

7 cm

$9 \times 9 = 81$

$5 \times 7 = 35$

> I can multiply the side lengths to find the areas of the large rectangle and the unshaded rectangle.

Area of the shaded figure: __81__ – __35__ = __46__

Area of the shaded figure: __46__ square centimeters

> I can subtract the area of the unshaded rectangle from the area of the large rectangle. That helps me find just the area of the shaded figure.

3. The figure shows a small rectangle cut out of a big rectangle.

3 ft   __4__ ft

6 ft   __4__ ft

2 ft

7 ft

> I can label this as 4 ft because the opposite side of the rectangle is 6 ft. Since opposite sides of rectangles are equal, I can subtract the known part of this side length, 2 ft, from the opposite side length, 6 ft. $6 \text{ ft} - 2 \text{ ft} = 4 \text{ ft}$. I can use a similar strategy to find the other unknown measurement: $7 \text{ ft} - 3 \text{ ft} = 4 \text{ ft}$.

a. Label the unknown measurements.

b. Area of the big rectangle: __6__ ft × __7__ ft = __42__ sq ft

c. Area of the small rectangle: __4__ ft × __4__ ft = __16__ sq ft

d. Find the area of just the shaded part.

$42 \text{ sq ft} - 16 \text{ sq ft} = 26 \text{ sq ft}$

The area of the shaded figure is 26 sq ft

> I can subtract the area of the small rectangle from the area of the big rectangle to find the area of just the shaded part.

Lesson 10:   Find areas by decomposing into rectangles or completing composite figures to form rectangles.

© Great Minds PBC TEKS Edition | greatminds.org/Texas

EUREKA MATH
TEKS EDITION

Name _____   Date _____

1. Each of the following figures is made up of 2 rectangles. Find the total area of each figure.

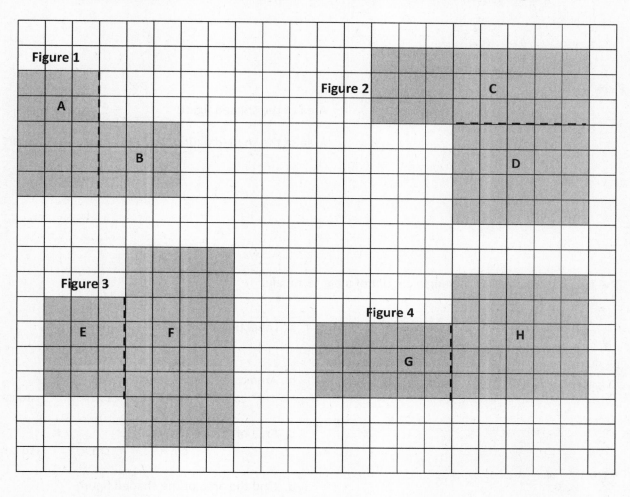

Figure 1: Area of A + Area of B: _____ sq units + _____ sq units = _____ sq units

Figure 2: Area of C + Area of D: _____ sq units + _____ sq units = _____ sq units

Figure 3: Area of E + Area of F: _____ sq units + _____ sq units = _____ sq units

Figure 4: Area of G + Area of H: _____ sq units + _____ sq units = _____ sq units

EUREKA
MATH
TEKS EDITION

Lesson 10:   Find areas by decomposing into rectangles or completing composite
figures to form rectangles.

143

© Great Minds PBC TEKS Edition |
greatminds.org/Texas

2. The figure shows a small rectangle cut out of a big rectangle. Find the area of the shaded figure.

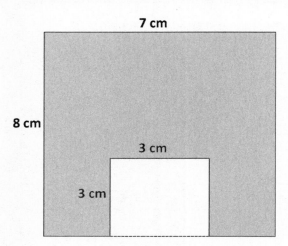

7 cm

8 cm

3 cm

3 cm

Area of the shaded figure: _____ – _____ = _____

Area of the shaded figure: _____ square centimeters

3. The figure shows a small rectangle cut out of a big rectangle.

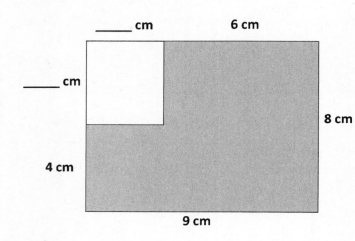

_____ cm   **6 cm**

_____ cm

8 cm

4 cm

9 cm

a. Label the unknown measurements.

b. Area of the big rectangle:
   _____ cm × _____ cm = _____ sq cm

c. Area of the small rectangle:
   _____ cm × _____ cm = _____ sq cm

d. Find the area of the shaded figure.

Lesson 10:   Find areas by decomposing into rectangles or completing composite figures to form rectangles.

EUREKA MATH
TEKS EDITION

1. Find the area of the following figure, which is made up of rectangles.

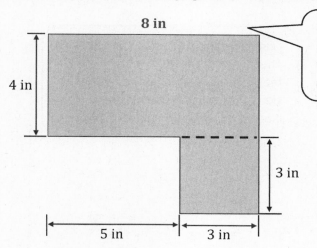

I can label this unknown side length as 8 inches because the opposite side is 5 inches and 3 inches, which makes a total of 8 inches. Opposite sides of a rectangle are equal.

$4 \times 8 = 32$

$3 \times 3 = 9$

$32 + 9 = ?$

31 1

$1 + 9 = 10$

$31 + 10 = 41$

I can find the area of the figure by finding the areas of the two rectangles and then adding. I can use a number bond to make adding easier.

The area of the figure is 41 square inches.

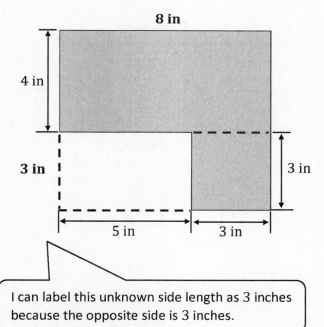

I can label this unknown side length as 3 inches because the opposite side is 3 inches.

$8 \times 7 = 56$

$3 \times 5 = 15$

$56 - 15 = 41$

Or, I can find the area of the figure by drawing lines to complete the large rectangle. Then I can find the areas of the large rectangle and the unshaded part. I can subtract the area of the unshaded part from the area of the large rectangle. Either way I solve, the area of the figure is 41 square inches.

Lesson 11:   Find areas by decomposing into rectangles or completing composite figures to form rectangles.

145

2. The figure below shows a small rectangle cut out of a big rectangle. Find the area of the shaded region.

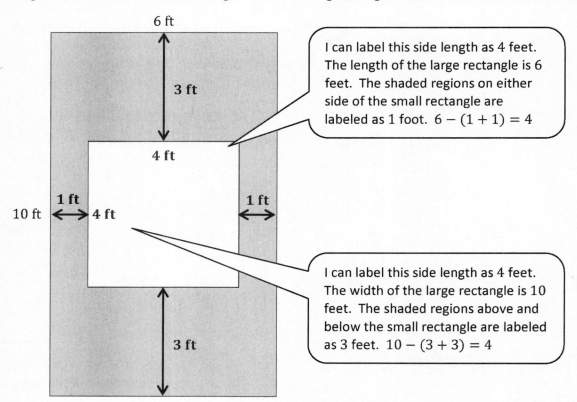

I can label this side length as 4 feet. The length of the large rectangle is 6 feet. The shaded regions on either side of the small rectangle are labeled as 1 foot. $6 - (1 + 1) = 4$

I can label this side length as 4 feet. The width of the large rectangle is 10 feet. The shaded regions above and below the small rectangle are labeled as 3 feet. $10 - (3 + 3) = 4$

$10 \times 6 = 60$

$4 \times 4 = 16$

$60 - 16 = ?$

40   20

I can find the areas of the large rectangle and the unshaded rectangle. Then I can subtract the area of the unshaded rectangle from the area of the large rectangle to find the area of the shaded region.

I can use a number bond to make the subtraction easier.

$20 - 16 = 4$

$40 + 4 = 44$

The area of the shaded region is 44 square feet.

Lesson 11:   Find areas by decomposing into rectangles or completing composite figures to form rectangles.

EUREKA MATH
TEKS EDITION

Name _____   Date _____

1. Find the area of each of the following figures. All figures are made up of rectangles.

a.

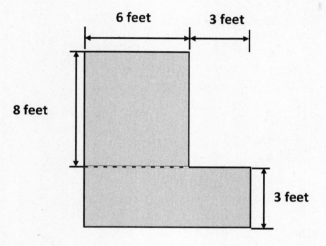

b.

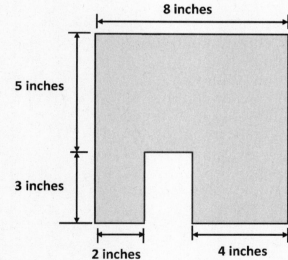

Lesson 11:   Find areas by decomposing into rectangles or completing composite
figures to form rectangles.

147

© Great Minds PBC TEKS Edition |
greatminds.org/Texas

2. The figure below shows a small rectangle cut out of a big rectangle.

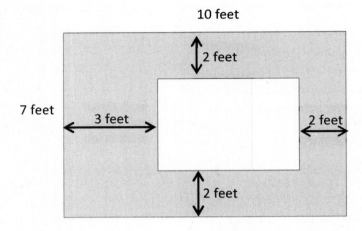

a. Label the side lengths of the unshaded region.

b. Find the area of the shaded region.

Lesson 11:   Find areas by decomposing into rectangles or completing composite
figures to form rectangles.

Use a ruler to measure the side lengths of each numbered room in the floor plan in centimeters. Then, find each area. Use the measurements below to match and label the rooms.

Kitchen/Living Room: 78 square centimeters

Bathroom: 24 square centimeters

Bedroom: 48 square centimeters

Hallway: 6 square centimeters

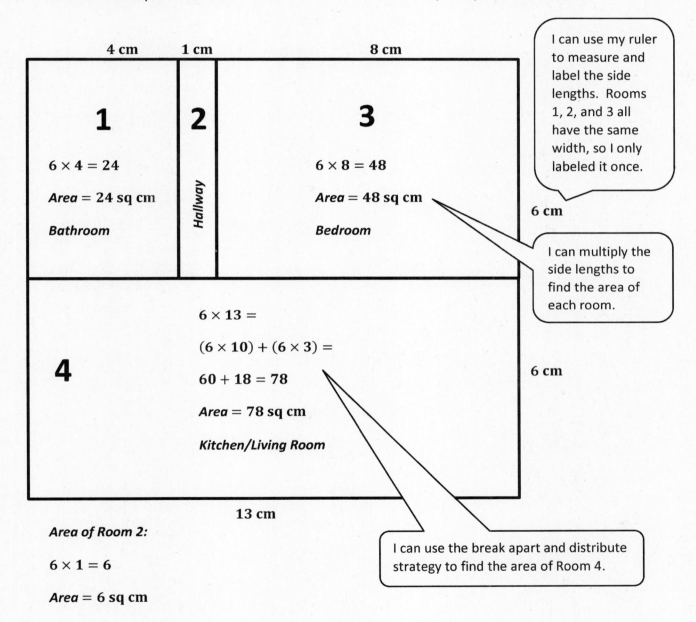

4 cm   **1 cm**   **8 cm**

1   **2**   **3**

$6 \times 4 = 24$

Area = 24 sq cm

Bathroom

Hallway

$6 \times 8 = 48$

Area = 48 sq cm

Bedroom

6 cm

I can use my ruler to measure and label the side lengths. Rooms 1, 2, and 3 all have the same width, so I only labeled it once.

I can multiply the side lengths to find the area of each room.

4

$6 \times 13 =$

$(6 \times 10) + (6 \times 3) =$

$60 + 18 = 78$

Area = 78 sq cm

Kitchen/Living Room

6 cm

13 cm

Area of Room 2:

$6 \times 1 = 6$

Area = 6 sq cm

I can use the break apart and distribute strategy to find the area of Room 4.

Lesson 12: Apply knowledge of area to determine areas of rooms in a given floor plan.

149

Name _____   Date _____

Use a ruler to measure the side lengths of each numbered room in centimeters. Then, find the area. Use the measurements below to match, and label the rooms with the correct areas.

Kitchen: 45 square centimeters   Living Room: 63 square centimeters

Porch: 34 square centimeters   Bedroom: 56 square centimeters

Bathroom: 24 square centimeters   Hallway: 12 square centimeters

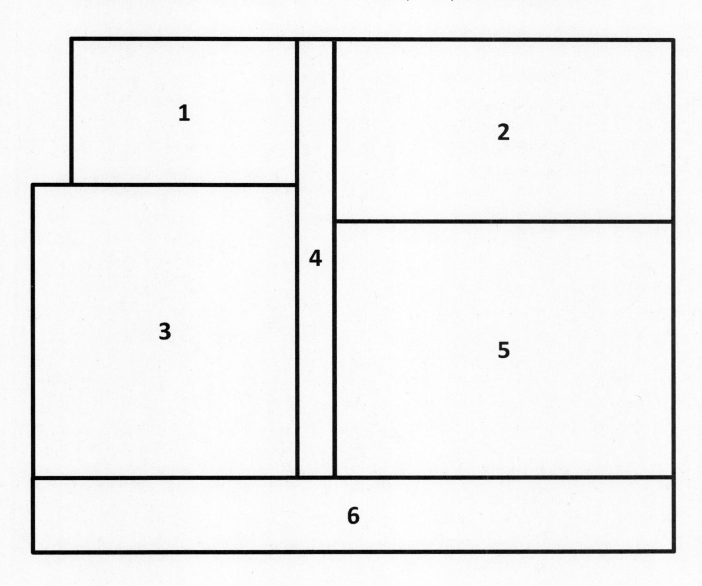

Lesson 12:   Apply knowledge of area to determine areas of rooms in a given floor plan.

© Great Minds PBC TEKS Edition | greatminds.org/Texas

151

Mrs. Harris designs her dream classroom on grid paper. The chart shows how much space she gives for each rectangular area. Use the information in the chart to draw and label a possible design for Mrs. Harris's classroom.

Reading area	48 square units	6 × 8
Carpet area	72 square units	9 × 8
Student desk area	90 square units	10 × 9
Science area	56 square units	7 × 8
Math area	64 square units	8 × 8

> I can think of multiplication facts that equal each area. Then I can use the multiplication facts as the side lengths of each rectangular area. I can use the grid to help me draw each rectangular area.

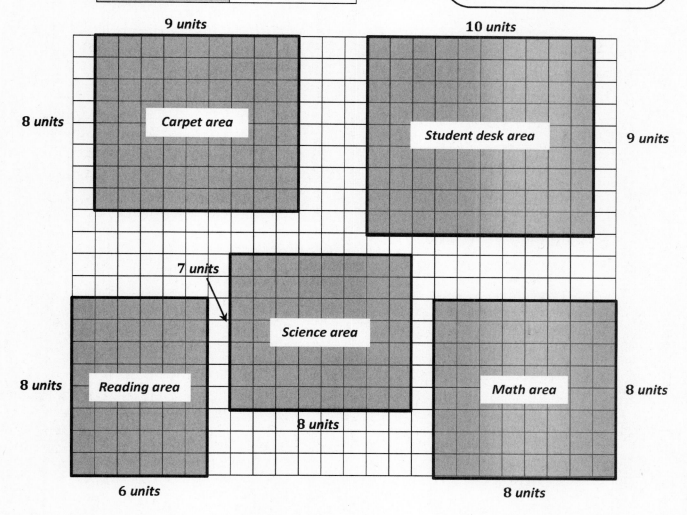

Lesson 13: Apply knowledge of area to determine areas of rooms in a given floor plan.

© Great Minds PBC TEKS Edition |
greatminds.org/Texas

153

Name _____   Date _____

Jeremy plans and designs his own dream playground on grid paper. His new playground will cover a total area of 100 square units. The chart shows how much space he gives for each piece of equipment, or area. Use the information in the chart to draw and label a possible way Jeremy can plan his playground.

Basketball court	10 square units
Jungle gym	9 square units
Slide	6 square units
Soccer area	24 square units

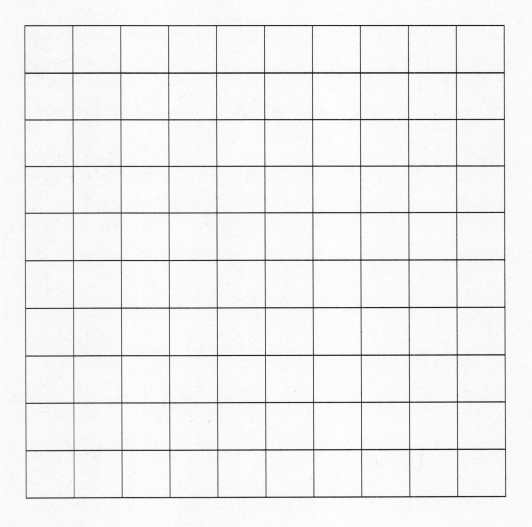

Lesson 13:   Apply knowledge of area to determine areas of rooms in a given floor plan.

© Great Minds PBC TEKS Edition |
greatminds.org/Texas

155